MORE ADVANCED
POWER SUPPLY
PROJECTS

G000077182

R. A. PENFOLD

BERNARD BABANI (publishing) LTD
THE GRAMPIANS
SHEPHERDS BUSH ROAD
LONDON W6 7NF
ENGLAND

PLEASE NOTE

Although every care has been taken with the production of this book to ensure that any projects, designs, modifications and/or programs etc. contained herein, operate in a correct and safe manner and also that any components specified are normally available in Great Britain, the Publishers do not accept responsibility in any way for the failure, including fault in design, of any project, design, modification or program to work correctly or to cause damage to any other equipment that it may be connected to or used in conjunction with, or in respect of any other damage or injury that may be so caused, nor do the Publishers accept responsibility in any way for the failure to obtain specified components.

Notice is also given that if equipment that is still under warranty is modified in any way or used or connected with home-built equipment then that warranty may be void.

IMPORTANT WARNING

Some of the projects in this book involve mains circuitry and it is strongly recommended that these should not be attempted by beginners or those with little knowledge or experience of electronic project construction. Do not attempt these projects unless you are certain that you know what you are doing. Never use components on mains circuitry projects that are in any way seconds or are of dubious manufacture or origin or differ from the specification of those recommended by the author.

First Published — January 1988
Reprinted — December 1990

British Library Cataloguing in Publication Data
Penfold, R. A.
    More advanced power supply projects.
    1. Electronic apparatus and appliances — Power supplies
    2. Electronic — Amateurs' manuals
    I. Title
        621.381'044   TK9965

ISBN 0 85934 166 6

Printed and Bound in Great Britain by Cox & Wyman Ltd, Reading

CONTENTS

Chapter 1   **Page**

    MISCELLANEOUS CIRCUITS 1
    Facts and Figures 4
    The L200 8
    Current Regulator 11
    Dimmer Circuits 11
    Touch Dimmer 17
    Dual Tracking 22
    Variable Tracking 24
    Battery Back-Up 30
    The ICL7673 33
    Adjustable Zener 36
    Reference Source 40
    Supply Monitoring 41

Chapter 2

    SWITCH MODE POWER SUPPLIES 45
    Drawbacks 45
    Advantages 46
    PWM 48
    Supply Configuration 51
    Output Stages 51
    Step-Up Circuit 54
    Inverter 55
    The TL497 57
    Step-Down Circuit 62
    Step-Up Circuit 63
    Higher Power 71
    Inductors 71
    Other Types 73

Chapter 3

    COMPUTER CONTROLLED SUPPLIES 78
    Switched Voltages 79
    Digital Control 79
    D/A Conversion 83
    Driving The Unit 90

Pinout details for semiconductors that have not been
covered previously 92

PREFACE

Although intended first and foremost as a follow up to book BP76 "Power Supply Projects" by the same author and publishers as this book, this book should be of interest to anyone who has a reasonable knowledge of power supply basics, and would like to learn about recent developments and more advanced forms of power supply. The practical and theoretical aspects of the circuits are covered in some detail, and the reader is not assumed to have an in-depth knowledge of electronic circuit design. However, anyone who is not familiar with the fundamentals of power supply design and operation would be well advised to consult a copy of BP76 before proceding to use this publication. Otherwise it is very much a matter of "learning to walk before you can crawl".

Some of the topics covered are simply recent developments that were not included in the original book, rather than circuits that are of a truely advanced nature. Three terminal adjustable voltage regulators fall into this category. Most of the subjects covered in this book are of a slightly more advanced nature though, including such things as a range of switched mode power supplies, precision regulators, dual tracking regulators, and computer controlled supplies. The circuits provided in this publication should satiate the vast majority of power supply needs that were not satisfied by its predecessor.

R. A. Penfold

ALSO OF INTEREST

BP76   Power Supply Projects

Chapter 1

MISCELLANEOUS CIRCUITS

In this chapter we will consider a variety of power supply related circuits, including three terminal variable voltage regulators, dual tracking regulators, and touch controlled dimmer circuits. We will start with three terminal voltage regulators.

Three terminal fixed voltage regulators and four terminal variable voltage types were covered in "Power Supply Projects". The three terminal adjustable type could be regarded as a cross between the two earlier types. All are series regulators, and the standard three terminal type are used in the manner shown in Figure 1(a). The effect of the regulator is simply to provide a series resistance that causes a voltage drop that gives the required output voltage. As the load current varies or the input voltage fluctuates, the series resistance of the regulator is adjusted by a feedback action so that there is no significant variation in the output voltage. This does, of course, assume that the input voltage is high enough to maintain the required output voltage, and that the output current does not exceed the maximum current rating of the regulator.

The four terminal regulators are conventional feedback types, but with the feedback input made accessible to the user rather than being fed via an internal potential divider (as in the three terminal regulators). The action of the device is to maintain the feedback terminal at a certain voltage, which is generally 5 volts for positive regulators, and −2.23 volts for the negative variety. With the feedback input connected direct to the output of the device the output is consequently maintained at the +5 or −2.23 volt level. Taking the feedback via a potential divider results in a voltage drop between the output and the feedback input. The output voltage therefore goes to a higher level in order to bring the potential at the feedback input up to the required level.

With suitable potential divider values the output voltage can be raised to any figure higher than the feedback input

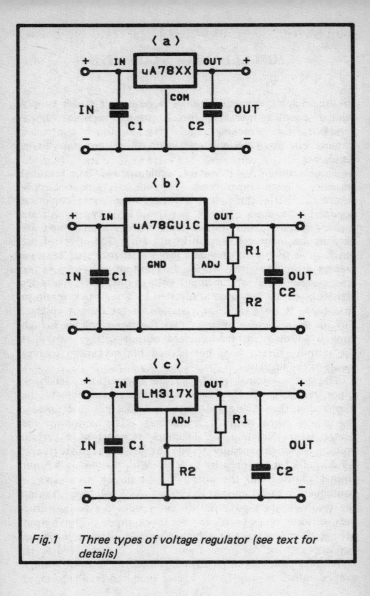

Fig. 1 Three types of voltage regulator (see text for details)

2

potential, but the monolithic regulators are only able to work safely at output potentials of up to 30 volts. The output is stabilised at the boosted voltage since the feedback action still functions much as before. Although the losses through the potential divider do admittedly reduce the regulation efficiency slightly, a well designed regulator of this type will work well at output voltages of at least ten times the feedback input potential.

With the three terminal adjustable regulators the basic action provided is very much the same as for a standard three terminal type. In fact the way in which they are used is much the same as for a non-adjustable type when it is connected in the "boosted" mode (as in Figure 23 of book BP76 for example). The idea of the boosted mode of operation is to raise the "common" terminal above the earth rail potential, so that the stabilised output voltage is stabilised at a level which is boosted by the same amount. This does not work particularly well with ordinary three terminal regulators as they consume relatively high supply currents, and the supply current varies substantially with variations in output loading. This makes it difficult to accurately maintain the "common" terminal at the required voltage. It can be done, but only by using relatively expensive circuitry that would make it point-less to do so. The normal boosted mode of operation is useful, but only in undemanding applications. Also, this mode of operation is normally only practical if a modest boost in the output voltage is all that is required.

The three terminal adjustable voltage regulators achieve a high standard of performance by having a supply current that is measured in microamps rather than milliamps. Provided the values in the potential divider circuit are reasonably low, the current flow through R2 is largely the current that flows through both R1 and R2 and is supplied by the output of the regulator. The amount of current flowing through R2 and into the "adjust" terminal is minute by comparison, and any changes in this current, even if by as much as (say) 50%, will not greatly affect the "adjust" terminal voltage (or the output voltage).

Facts and Figures

That is the basis of their operation, but how are the values for R1 and R2 determined, and how well do these regulators perform in practice? The mathematics are very simple, and these devices provide an excellent standard of performance.

Starting with the determination of the resistor values, there is some latitude as to the current that should flow through R1 and R2. In the interest of good regulation efficiency this current should be as high as possible so that the supply current of the regulator is as small as possible by comparison. On the other hand, this current should not be so large that it constitutes a large proportion of the available output current! The output is stabilised at 1.2 volts above the "adjust" terminal potential, and a current of 5 milliamps is the current normally used through the potential divider circuit. This sets the value of R1 at 240 ohms (1.2 volts divided by 0.005 amps = 240 ohms).

The value of R2 must be selected to give the desired output voltage, and it is quite easy to determine the required value. With a 5 milliamp current flow there is 1 volt developed across R2 per 200 ohms of resistance. The output voltage is 1.2 volts more than the voltage developed across R2. Therefore, the required value is calculated by deducting 1.2 volts from the desired output voltage, and then multiplying this figure by 200. This gives an answer in ohms.

As a simple example, assume that an output potential of 10 volts is required. Deducting 1.2 volts from 10 volts gives 8.8 volts, and multiplying this by 200 produces a final answer of 1760 ohms (1.76k). The nearest preferred value to 1.76k is 1.8k, which would give an output voltage very close to the required figure of 10 volts. However, as with other forms of adjustable voltage regulator, where very accurate results are required it is necessary to use a preset resistor, and to trim the output voltage to precisely the correct level.

Like other integrated circuit voltage regulators, the three terminal adjustable types require input and output decoupling capacitors in order to ensure stable operation. Figure 2 gives an example circuit, and this is for a nominal 1.2 to 6.2 volt variable supply.

The positive three terminal adjustable regulators are the

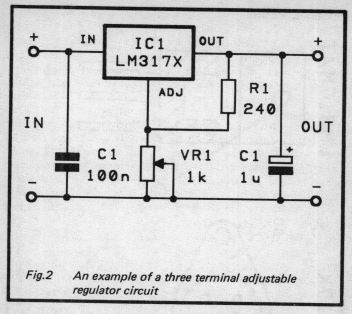

Fig.2   *An example of a three terminal adjustable regulator circuit*

LM317 series, and these have a suffix letter which indicates the maximum output current and case style, as shown in Table 1.

Table 1

Device	Max.Current	Drop-Out V.	Case	Max. Power
LM317L	100mA	1.8V	TO92	0.625W
LM317M	500mA	1.8V	TO220	12W
LM317T	1.5A	2.25V	TO220	15W
LM317K	1.5A	2.5V	TO3	20W

With the higher current types it is obviously essential to use adequate heatsinking, especially where the voltage drop through the device is large and the power dissipation is high. The maximum power dissipation ratings for all four components are included in Table 1. The output voltage range for all these regulators is 1.2 to 37 volts, and the maximum input to

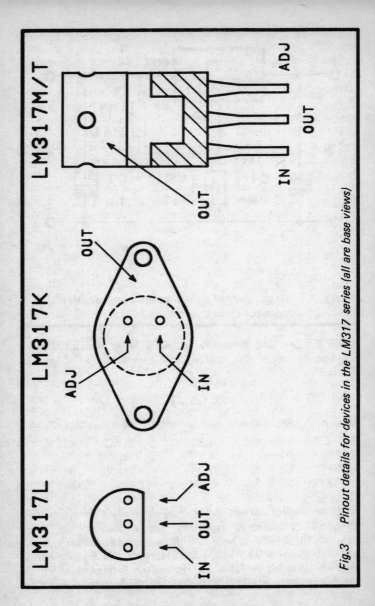

Fig.3   Pinout details for devices in the LM317 series (all are base views)

6

output voltage differential is 40 volts. Figure 3 gives pinout details for all four types.

The performance of these regulators is extremely good. The drop-out voltages are quite low, as detailed in Table 1. Load and line regulation are 0.1% and 0.01% respectively for all four types. The ripple rejection is an impressive 65dB, and this figure is again common to all four components.

With four terminal regulators, or any regulators of this general type, the feedback is sometimes taken from close to the output load. The point of this is that the feedback action then compensates for any voltage drop through the wiring between the supply and the load, giving superior regulation. This method is not recommended with the three terminal adjustable regulators which operate on what is a slightly different principle. This is particularly important where the output voltage is many times higher than the basic 1.2 volt output of the device. The reason for this is that any voltage drop through the output wiring would effectively be added to the 1.2 volt reference level. If the output voltage is (say) twenty times this 1.2 volt level, then the output voltage should be 24 volts. If there was a voltage drop of 0.1 volts through the wiring, this would give an effective reference voltage of 1.3 volts, and an actual output potential of approximately 26 volts. This compares with 23.9 volts if the feedback was taken direct from the output of the regulator. Clearly, for optimum performance the feedback should be taken from as close to the output of the regulator as possible.

The LM317 series of regulators incorporate output current limiting, but it is important to note that this is not of the "foldback" type (as used in most other integrated circuit voltage regulators). The output current under short circuit conditions can be up to about 60% higher than the maximum current rating of the component, and under these conditions the power dissipation can be very high. This might not matter in some applications, and is unlikely to be of significance where a regulator is used well below its maximum output current rating. However, when using one of these components near its current limit it is a good idea to use a heatsink of generous rating together with an ordinary fuse to cut the supply if an overload should last for more than a fraction of a second.

As yet there does not seem to be any negative versions of the three terminal adjustable voltage regulators, although these will no doubt appear in due course. There is a very useful high power version (the LM338K) which has a 1.2 to 32 volt output range and a maximum output current of some 5 amps. It has a TO3 encapsulation with the same pinout configuration as the LM317K, but with an impressive maximum power dissipation rating of 50 watts. Note that its maximum input to output voltage difference is only 35 volts (and not 40 volts as for the LM317 series), and its drop-out voltage is 2.9 volts. The LM338K is used in exactly the same manner as the LM317 series of regulators, and its level of performance is very similar.

The L200

The L200 is a very high performance voltage/current regulator and although it is not exactly a new device, it has received remarkably little coverage in the technical press for a device of such quality and usefulness. Its main claim to fame is its current limiting, power limiting, thermal shutdown, and input over-voltage protection circuits. These render the device virtually indestructible! It has an excellent specification apart from this, and it also has the very attractive feature of adjustable output current limiting. Its only drawback is that it is slightly more expensive than the standard four terminal voltage regulators, although its added features would seem to justify the higher cost.

Due to this programmable output current capability, the L200 requires a five pin package. This is a sort of "stretched" "plastic power" type encapsulation, and is much the same as the "pentawatt" package used for some popular audio power amplifier integrated circuits. Figure 4 gives input details for the L200, which is effectively an ordinary four terminal regulator, but with an additional terminal to facilitate programming of the limit current.

The performance figures of the L200 are quite good, and it has an output voltage range of 2.85 to 36 volts. The input voltage range is 4.85 to 40 volts. The line and load regulation are 0.1% and 0.03% respectively. The maximum output

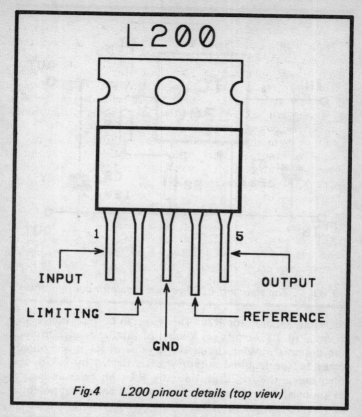

Fig.4   L200 pinout details (top view)

current is 2 amps, and the short circuit current is given as 2.5 amps.   Note that the L200 does not have foldback current limiting, and it would be unusable as a current regulator if it did.   The ripple rejection is typically 70dB, and the output noise is only 80 microvolts. The quiescent current consumption is approximately 4.2 milliamps.

The basic regulator circuit for the device is shown in Figure 5. R1 and R2 set the output voltage in standard four terminal regulator fashion.   The reference voltage of the L200 is 2.77 volts, and the current through the potential divider circuit should be approximately 3 milliamps. A value of 820 ohms is

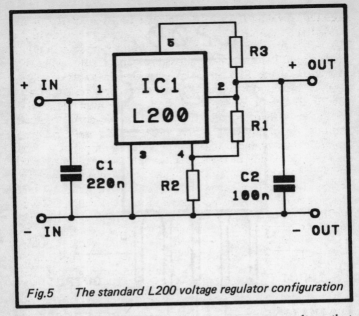

Fig.5   The standard L200 voltage regulator configuration

therefore suitable for R2. This gives an output voltage that
is equal to 3.378 volts per kilohm of total resistance through
the potential divider circuit. The value of R1 is accordingly
equal to the required output voltage divided by 3.378, and
then minus the 0.82k provided by R2 (this gives an answer
in kilohms). As an example, assume that an output potential
of 10 volts is required. 10 divided by 3.378 is (approximately)
2.96k, and deducting 0.82k from this gives a final answer
of 2.14k. The nearest preferred value to this calculated
figure is 2.2k, but obviously a preset resistor should be used
if a high degree of accuracy is required.

Calculating the required value for R3 is quite straight
forward, and the correct value for this component is obtained
by dividing 0.45 by the required maximum output current.
Assuming the output current is in amps, this gives an answer
in ohms. If the current is in milliamps, then the value obtained for R3 is in kilohms. As an example of calculating the
value of R3, if a maximum output current of 1.5 amps is

required, dividing 0.45 by 1.5 gives an answer of 0.3 ohms.

Although 0.3 ohms is theoretically a preferred value in the E24 series of values, in practice it is unlikely that such a low value would be obtainable. Most low value resistor ranges are restricted to the E12 range, or even the E6 series of values. Using a preset resistor might not be practical either, as very low value preset resistors are not readily available, and it could be difficult to adjust a preset for the correct current limiting figure anyway. Where necessary R3 must be made up from two or more resistors in series or in parallel. With our example value of 0.3 ohms it would be possible to make up the required value from two 0.15 ohm resistors wired in series. Bear in mind that with an output current of 1 amp the power dissipated in R3 can be around 0.5 watts, and with an output current of 2 amps it is closer to 1 watt. The resistor or resistors used in the R3 position must therefore be of adequate power rating if the circuit is used at high output currents. Also, IC1 must obviously be fitted on an adequate heatsink if it is operated under conditions that cause it to dissipate more than about 1 watt.

Current Regulator
The L200 can operate as a current regulator if it is connected in the configuration shown in Figure 6. This is actually much the same as the standard voltage regulator circuit, but the feedback input has been connected to earth so that the output goes fully positive. The current limit circuit of IC1 then holds the output voltage at a level that gives the required current flow. The value of R1 is therefore equal to 0.45 divided by the required output current (just as for R3 in the voltage regulator circuit of Figure 5). Of course, as is the case with any current regulator circuit, the set output current will only flow if the resistance across the output is sufficiently low to permit a current flow of this magnitude. It is no use setting R1 for a particular current if the maximum output voltage and load resistance do not permit a current flow of at least this amount.

Dimmer Circuits
Producing a power supply design does not necessarily mean

11

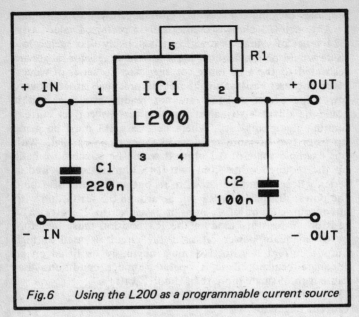

Fig.6   *Using the L200 as a programmable current source*

developing one having a well smoothed and regulated DC
output signal. Many applications require an attenuated AC
mains supply. This includes lamp dimmers, drill speed
controllers, etc. The obvious means of power control for
this type of thing is simply to use a high power variable
resistance (a "rheostat") in series with the supply, and
this method has actually been used a great deal in the past.

In more recent times it has been more normal to use
some form of semiconductor AC power controller. The
variable resistor approach to the problem has the advantage
of simplicity, but the variable resistor will usually have to
dissipate quite high power levels. This means using a
physically large component that is likely to be expensive
and difficult to obtain. A lot of power will be wasted, and
the heat generated by all this excess power also has to be
removed somehow.

Semiconductor AC power controllers offer a much better
means of control that enables moderately high powers to be

12

regulated by small devices that produce very little heat. This low level of heat generation means that little power is wasted. This efficiency is obtained by using a switching element to control the output power, rather than a dropper resistance. The basic idea is to only permit part of each half cycle to pass through to the output. Figure 7 shows typical output waveforms from a semiconductor 'dimmer' unit at (a) full power, (b) half power, and (c) minimum power.

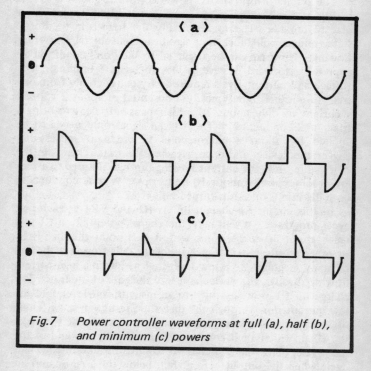

Fig.7   Power controller waveforms at full (a), half (b), and minimum (c) powers

In (a) the switch is activated almost at the beginning of each half cycle, and very little of the input waveform is cut out. There is usually some slight loss of power at maximum output, but this should not be sufficient to be noticeable. At half power the switch is not activated until half way through

13

each half cycle, and at minimum power the switch does not turn on until almost the end of each half cycle. Many AC power controllers will not give zero output, but at minimum power the output level is usually so low as to be totally insignificant. However, it is worth noting that some "dimmer" units have a minimum recommended load power, and if used with smaller loads they may fail to "dim" them properly when set for low output powers.

The standard form of AC power controller circuit is shown in Figure 8. This has a triac as the switching element and a diac to provide triggering. Initially the triac is in the "off" state, and it will block any significant output current from flowing. The triac can be triggered to the "on" condition by applying a forward or reverse bias to its gate terminal. The voltage and current levels required vary considerably from one triac to another, but typically a potential of about 2 volts at a current of only about 10 milliamps is sufficient to bring a triac into conduction. The trigger signal only needs to be applied for about a microsecond in order to successfully trigger the device, and once triggered the triac remains in the "on" state until the current flowing through it drops to a very low level (typically about 10 milliamps). A triac conducts in both directions once it is turned on.

In this circuit C1 charges up via R1 and VR1 as each half cycle progresses. Eventually the charge potential on C1 will reach about 30 to 35 volts, and at this point the diac fires. In other words, its resistance suddenly falls from a high level of many megohms to a low level that results in a high current flowing through the device and into the gate of the triac. The charge on C1 soon subsides to an insignificant level, and the low current flow through the diac then results in it switching off. However, the brief pulse of current is adequate to trigger the triac, which then conducts until virtually the end of the half cycle. The triac switches off towards the end of each half cycle when the output current falls below the hold-on current of the device.

The point at which the triac triggers in each half cycle depends on the setting of VR1. If this is set at minimum resistance, the charge voltage on C1 lags only marginally behind the AC input voltage. This voltage has a peak

14

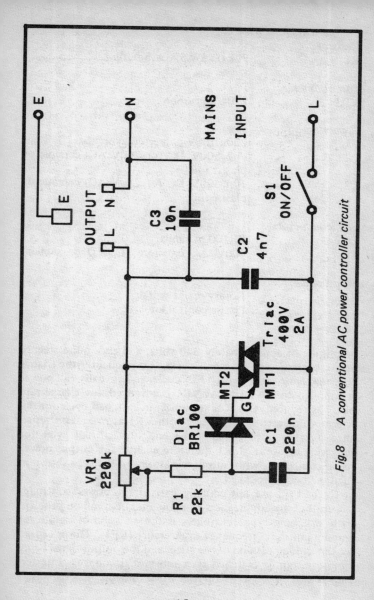

Fig.8   A conventional AC power controller circuit

15

Components for Figure 8
Resistor
R1   22k 0.25W 5% carbon film

Potentiometer
VR1   220k lin carbon

Capacitors
C1   220n 100V polyester layer
C2   4n7 500V DC (or 250V AC) ceramic or
                        plastic foil
C3   10n 500V DC (or 250V AC) ceramic or
                        plastic foil

Semiconductors
Diac   BR100 or similar
Triac   400V 2A or more (C206D or similar)

Miscellaneous
S1   Rotary mains switch
                        Plastic control knob

amplitude of approximately 340 volts, and rises quite steeply at the beginning of each half cycle. Consequently the triac is triggered very early in each half cycle, and virtually full power is supplied to the load. As VR1 is advanced, the charge rate of C1 is reduced, and it takes longer in each half cycle for the trigger voltage to be reached. With VR1 at maximum resistance it takes until virtually the end of each half cycle for triggering to occur. VR1 therefore enables the output power to be controlled, with output waveforms of the type shown in Figure 7 being produced.

C2 and C3 are not actually part of the power controller circuit, but are suppression components. A common problem with switching type controllers is the emission of significant amounts of radio frequency interference (RFI). This is caused by the sudden turn-on of the triac, and the output signal being almost instantly switched to a substantial voltage. Interference is at its worst at half power when the output signal jumps almost instantly to about 340 volts. The fast risetime and the high voltage results in strong harmonics of the 50Hz mains frequency being generated. These harmonics may well extend to frequencies of 1MHz or more. C2 and C3 provide a reasonable degree of suppression, but an AM broadcast receiver used very close to a power controller of this type will normally pick-up a certain amount of interference.

The circuit should work well using any triac that has an operating voltage of 400 volts or more, and a current rating of 2 amps or greater (a C206D is suitable).

Note that a few triacs have a built-in diac. These are suitable for use in this circuit, but R1 and C1 should then connect direct to the gate terminal of the triac, and the external diac should be omitted.

The constructional notes on the Touch Dimmer circuit (which is described next) largely apply to this project as well. **Read these notes carefully as any project which connects to the mains supply is potentially lethal, and the standard safety precautions must be taken when constructing and installing these two projects.**

Touch Dimmer

There are special AC controller integrated circuits available, and these provide more sophisticated control than a basic dimmer of the type described previously. The TEA1058 is one of the more interesting devices of this type, and one that seems to be readily available to amateur users. It enables the lamp (or other load) to be controlled via two touch contacts rather than by way of the more usual potentiometer. Figure 9 shows the circuit diagram for a touch dimmer based on the TEA1058.

The TEA1058 is a fairly complex device, but one which is reasonably simple as far as the user is concerned. The power fed to the load is varied in standard phase-type controller fashion, and an external triac is required. This is triggered from IC1 via current limiting resistor R7. L1 and C5 are suppressor components. A low voltage DC supply is required to power IC1, and this is derived from the mains supply by way of a simple rectifier and smoothing circuit based on D1, D2, and C2.

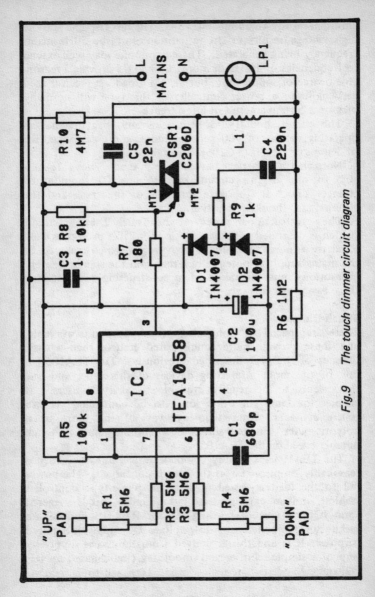

Fig.9   The touch dimmer circuit diagram

18

Components for Figure 9
Resistors (all 0.25W 5% except where noted)

R1, 2, 3, 4	5M6 (4 off)
R5	100k
R6	1M2
R7	180R
R8	10k
R9	1k 2 watt
R10	4M7

Capacitors

C1	680p polystyrene
C2	100μ 25V elect
C3	1n polyester layer
C4	220n 500V DC (or 250V AC) plastic foil
C5	22n 500V DC (or 250V AC) plastic foil

Semiconductors

IC1	TEA1058
D1, 2	1N4007 (2 off)
CSR1	400V 2A or more (C206D or similar)

Miscellaneous

L1	2A mains suppressor choke
LP1	Mains lamp (up to 200W)
	Touch pads, circuit board, etc.

IC1 must monitor the mains supply so that it can trigger the triac at the appropriate point in each half cycle. The mains signal is loosely coupled to an input on IC1 via R10, and C3 filters out any noise spikes on the supply which might otherwise prevent proper synchronisation from being obtained.

An obvious problem with a touch controlled dimmer is that of isolating the user from the dangerous mains supply. There are several quite involved and expensive ways of achieving this, but most touch dimmers seem to utilize a very simple but safe method. This is merely to have a very high input impedance for each touch contact so that a very high value resistance can be included between each touch pad and its input. The high input impedance ensures that there is no massive signal loss through each series resistor, and that the circuit is able to function properly. I suppose that strictly speaking the series resistors do not isolate the user from the mains supply, and that the user is in fact directly connected to the mains. However, with a resistance of several megohms and a mains supply of 240 volts AC, the high current flow needed to produce a severe electric shock can not flow. In fact the maximum current flow is restricted to a few tens of microamps at most, which is completely harmless.

In this circuit there are two touch contacts, and two 5M6 resistors connected in series with each one. This gives a total resistance of some 11M2 in series with each contact, which ensures good safety. The point of having two resistors is that the unit will still be safe to use if one of the resistors goes closed circuit. There will still be at least 5M6 between the user and the mains supply, and the maximum current flow will still be a matter of tens of microamps. **Do not replace R1 and R2 or R3 and R4 with a single high value resistor.**

There are separate "up" and "down" touch pads to control the brightness of the lamp. On the face of it there is no way that touching one of the pads can produce a signal that the TEA1058 can detect, but touching a contact results in mains "hum" picked up in the operator's body being coupled into the appropriate input of IC1. Circuits within IC1 then raise or lower the brightness of the lamp, and a simple memory circuit holds the unit at the current brightness level when the contact is released.

Actually the method of control is a little more sophisticated than just having basic "up" and "down" controls. When the unit is first connected to the mains supply the lamp is switched off. Touching one or both of the touch pads results in the lamp being switched on, but only at low brightness. The lamp brightness can then be increased by touching the "up" pad, or decreased by touching the "down" pad. The brightness can be faded down to a very low level, but it can not be switched off altogether. However, the TEA1058 incorporates on/off switching, and this is activated by briefly touching one or both touch contacts. This gives a sort of toggle action, and briefly touching a contact therefore switches the device to the opposite state — touching it again switches it back to its original state.

Although I have referred to the load as a lamp, it can of course be any other piece of equipment that can be used with dimmer units, such as an electric drill (but not fluorescent lamps). The C206D triac enables loads of up to about 200 watts to be handled without a heatsink, or 600 watts if it is fitted with a medium size heatsink. If the equipment fed from the unit has a three core mains cable it is essential for safety reasons to connect the mains earth through to the earth lead of the controlled equipment.

Although the two dimmer circuits featured here are not particularly complex projects, **due to the fact that they connect direct to the mains they can not be regarded as ideal for beginners. In fact they can only really be recommended to constructors with a reasonable amount of experience.** The unit must be housed in a case that has a screw fitting lid or cover so that there is no easy access to the dangerous mains wiring. With a little ingenuity the unit could probably be made small enough to fit into a standard light switch box. Any exposed metalwork must be earthed to the mains earth lead.

Of course, an exception to this is the touch contacts. It may be possible to obtain proper touch contacts, but these do not seem to be as widely available as they once were. An M4 panhead screw is a suitable substitute though, and a connection is easily made to one of these via a soldertag held in place by the fixing nut. The touch contacts must be mounted on a panel that is made from plastic or some other good insulator, or they must be reliably insulated from the front panel. The most important point to watch is that there is no easy way for the touch contacts to come into contact with any of the other components in the unit. The only sure way of achieving this is to use generous amounts of insulation tape over the rear of the contacts, or to find some similar means of insulating them.

Thoroughly check all the wiring for errors before testing the finished unit. With some projects a policy of try it first and check it later if necessary might be acceptable, but this is certainly not the case with a mains controller project such as

21

this. Always fit the lid or cover of the case in place before connecting the unit to the mains supply. Never touch any of the wiring or components when the unit is connected to the mains supply. To do so could be fatal. One final point is to refer carefully to the components list as not all the components are standard low wattage and low voltage types. L1 can be any mains suppression choke which has a current rating of at least 3 amps.

Dual Tracking
Many circuits, particularly those that are based on operational amplifiers, require dual balanced supply rails. One way of producing dual balanced supply rails is simply to have separate positive and negative supply circuits with a common earth (0 volt) supply rail. There will almost certainly be some slight imbalance in the supply voltages, but in practice this is not likely to be large enough to have any adverse effect on the powered equipment. In fact most dual supply rail equipment will work perfectly well with a massive mismatch in the supply voltages, but not all circuits are this accommodating. The only real drawbacks of this method are that overloads on the outputs can sometimes defeat the overload protection circuits and cause serious damage to one or both regulators. Also, this approach does not work well with variable voltage supplies, although it is possible to achieve reasonable accuracy using a dual gang potentiometer with one gang for each power supply circuit. However, better accuracy and more reliable operation are usually afforded by using a circuit specifically designed for dual supply applications.

Where a low power dual 15 volt supply is required the obvious choice is a circuit based on the 4195 dual 15 volt regulator. This device is contained in a standard 8 pin DIL plastic package, and it has the pinout configuration shown in Figure 10. When used as a straightforward dual 15 volt regulator only five terminals of the 4195 are actually used, as can be seen from the basic 4195 regulator circuit of Figure 11.

This device is obviously very easy to use, but a few points about this circuit have to be borne in mind when deciding whether or not it is suitable for a given task. The input voltage ranges are 18 to 30 volts and −18 to −30 volts, and

22

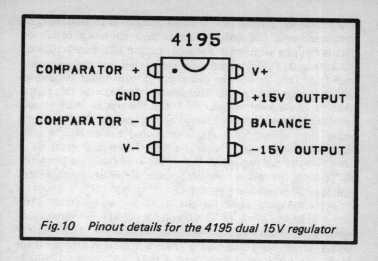

Fig.10   Pinout details for the 4195 dual 15V regulator

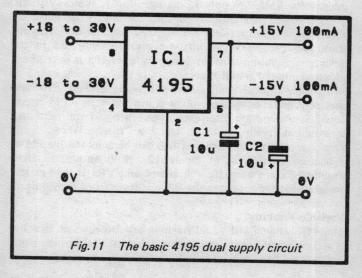

Fig.11   The basic 4195 dual supply circuit

23

the maximum output is 100 milliamps per rail. However, the only version of the device available through normal retail outlets is the one which has a standard 8 pin DIL plastic package (TO-99 and TO-66 metal packaged types are also manufactured). This proscribes using the device under conditions which give a high power dissipation. In practice this means that for an output current of 100 milliamps on both supply rails the input/output differential voltages must both be no more than about 5.5 volts, and should preferably be only about 4 to 4.5 volts. Note that the differential must be at least 3 volts per supply if the 4195 is to function properly. Of course, at lower output currents higher input/output voltage differentials are acceptable.

Performance figures for the 4195 are quite good. The line regulation for a 18 to 30 volts input voltage variation is typically 2 millivolts (20 millivolts maximum). Load regulation is nearly as good, and a change in output current from 1 to 100 milliamps gives a typical shift in the output voltage of only 5 millivolts (30 millivolts maximum). The output voltages are guaranteed to be within 500 millivolts of the nominal figures, and the typical output noise voltage is 60 microvolts RMS. Supply ripple rejection is typically 75dB.

The device has output current limiting, with a typical short circuit output current of 220 milliamps. Thermal shutdown protection circuits are also incorporated in the device. The supply current drawn by the 4195 is only about plus and minus 1.5 milliamps.

In some critical applications it may be necessary to have precisely matched output voltages, but the basic 4195 circuit could have a voltage difference of as much as 1 volt (although it would normally be much less than this). Where highly accurate matching is required this can be achieved by adding a balance control, as in Figure 12. Both outputs must be monitored using accurate voltmeters, and VR1 is then merely adjusted to give precisely the same voltage from each output.

Variable Tracking

The 4195 is a "fixed" dual tracking regulator, which in a way is a contradiction in terms, as the "tracking" part of the name suggests that the output voltage is variable, and as one voltage

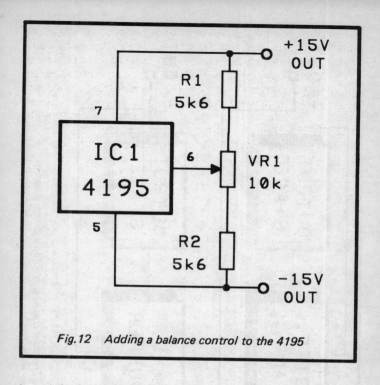

Fig.12 Adding a balance control to the 4195

is varied, the other output potential automatically adjusts to its complement. Variable dual tracking supplies are perfectly feasible, and can be implemented much more simply than one might expect. The block diagram of Figure 13 shows the standard arrangement for a variable dual tracking supply.

A conventional positive voltage regulator is formed by the top three blocks, and the output voltage can be made variable by the usual means of including a potentiometer in the feedback circuit to the differential amplifier. The inverting buffer stage is an operational inverting amplifier which has a voltage gain of unity, and its non-inverting input biased to the central 0 volt supply rail. The input of the amplifier is fed from the output of the positive supply circuit. This gives the desired

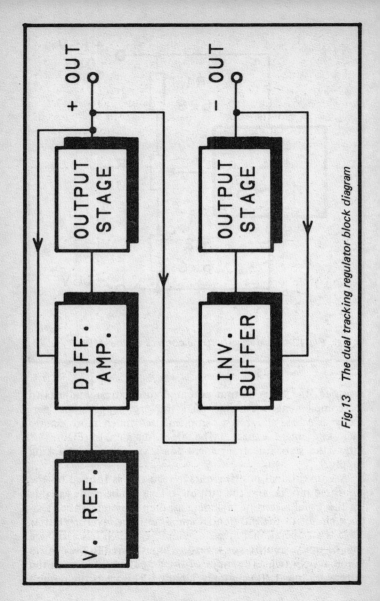

Fig.13   The dual tracking regulator block diagram

tracking effect, with a negative output voltage that is an exact complement of the positive input potential. The maximum output current available from the operational amplifier will be inadequate for most purposes, but an output buffer stage can be used to boost the available output current to a suitable level. Note though, that the output stage should be included in the negative feedback circuit of the inverting amplifier so that the feedback compensates for the voltage drop through the output stage and maintains accurate tracking.

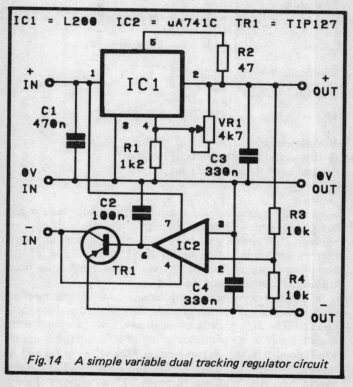

Fig.14   A simple variable dual tracking regulator circuit

Figure 14 shows the circuit diagram for a variable dual tracking regulator which is based on an SGS-ATES application circuit for the L200 regulator chip. The part of the circuit

27

Components for Figure 14
Resistors (all 0.25W 5% carbon unless noted)
R1   1K2
R2   47R (see text)
R3, 4   10k (2 off) (1% tolerance)

Potentiometer
VR1   4k7 lin carbon

Capacitors
C1   470n polyester layer
C2   100n ceramic
C3, 4   330n polyester layer (2 off)

Semiconductors
IC1   L200
IC2   µA741C
TR1   TIP127

Miscellaneous
Heatsinks and insulating sets (if required)
Control knob, circuit board, etc.

around IC1 is actually just a standard L200 adjustable regulator circuit which gives an output voltage range of approximately 2.77 volts to 13.5 volts. R2 sets the maximum output current at around 100 milliamps, but the value of this component can be altered to give any desired limit figure within the capabilities of the L200.

IC2 operates as the basis of the unity voltage gain inverting mode amplifier, and this is a standard operational amplifier circuit. The only slightly unusual aspect of the circuit is the inclusion of C2 in the output circuit of IC2, and this is needed to aid good stability. It is the ratio of the values of R3 and R4 that determine the voltage gain of the circuit, and in order to ensure accurate tracking these should accordingly have a tolerance of 1%. If absolute accuracy is essential, simply replace one of these resistors with a 6.8k fixed resistor and a 4.7k preset wired in series, and then adjust the preset for optimum tracking accuracy. Of course, if highly accurate tracking is not needed it is then in order to use standard 5% components. TR1 is an emitter follower output stage, and this provides output currents of up to 2 amps (which matches the limit imposed on the positive supply rail by IC1). The TIP127 specified for the TR1 position is a Darlington power device incidentally, and an ordinary PNP power transistor is not a suitable substitute.

Once again, a few points need to be kept in mind when using this circuit. Firstly, the absolute maximum input voltage is plus and minus 18 volts, which is the limit imposed by IC2. It is preferable to leave a safety margin though, and an input of plus and minus 16 volts is a more realistic maximum. The maximum dropout voltage of the L200 is 2.5 volts, but the negative supply generator circuit is somewhat less efficient and its dropout voltage is around 3.5 volts. This makes it difficult to obtain sufficient "headroom" to produce the full 13.6 volt output level, but if necessary IC2 can be replaced with a CA3140E. This reduces the dropout voltage of the negative supply circuit to about 2 volts.

The positive supply circuit has the current limiting provided by the L200, but as the circuit stands there is no current limiting on the negative supply. There is only overload protection on the negative supply in that an overload on the positive supply will cause its output voltage to fall, and the negative supply potential will also fall as it tracks the positive rail in the normal way. An overload on the negative supply will not cause any similar tracking by the positive supply circuit incidentally. In some applications the lack of current limiting on the negative supply will not be of major importance, but it is crucial in an application such as a bench power supply where frequent overloads are almost inevitable.

It is not difficult to add current limiting to the circuit using conventional techniques. The most simple way of tackling the problem is to provide the negative input supply via a voltage regulator which incorporates current limiting. A −15 volt monolithic regulator should suffice. It would be possible to incorporate a simple current limiting circuit into the output stage of the circuit using the same basic technique as that utilized in the train controller circuit (Figure 33 of book

BP76). However, this would have a slight disadvantage in that it would increase the dropout voltage of the negative supply circuit.

Construction of the unit should not prove to be difficult, but remember that IC1 and TR1 must be mounted on adequate heatsinks if the unit is used with output currents of more than about 70 milliamps. Also keep in mind that the collector of TR1 connects internally to its heat-tab, and that the earth connection of IC1 (pin 3) connects to its heat-tab. It is unlikely that IC1 will need to be insulated from its heatsink, but TR1 probably will require the use of a standard "plastic power" insulating set. If either device needs to be insulated from its heatsink, before switching on check with a continuity tester to ensure that the insulation is effective. The plastic insulating washers are necessarily very thin, and are easily damaged.

Battery Back-Up

It is now common practice to have digital circuits that incorporate a clock/calendar circuit and (or) some random access memory (RAM) that stores system information. For example, I have three different computers that are fitted with the MC146818 clock/calendar/RAM device. Apart from providing date and time information to applications programs and the operating system, the RAM in this device is normally used to provide start-up information to the operating system. Typically this information would be such things as the initial screen mode, information on the types of disc drive present in the system, the amount of RAM fitted, and things of this type.

Obviously the clock/calendar circuit will only function while it is provided with power, and the RAM is almost invariably of the volatile variety. This simply means that it suffers from severe amnesia as soon as the power is cut off. As a result of this, power must be maintained to the clock/calendar/RAM circuits when the equipment is switched off, or everything must be reset each time the equipment is switched on!

A little used solution to the problem is to have a small mains power supply circuit that remains switched on and supplying power to the RAM (or whatever) when the equipment is switched off. I have a microprocessor controlled short wave radio which uses this system with reasonable success, but it still has the more popular system of a battery to power the RAM when mains power is absent. The problem with a back-up mains supply is that it is defeated if someone should unplug the equipment from the mains supply, or there should be a brief mains failure. There is also a slight safety problem, in that it is not generally considered good practice to have mains powered equipment left running for long periods unattended.

Battery back-up can only work well if the RAM or other circuit powered by the battery has a very low current consumption. A battery of moderate capacity such as three or four HP7 size cells should then provide virtually their "shelf" life, which in practice generally means about 6 to 12 months of operation. The RAM used in this type of application is the CMOS static type, which has an extremely low current consumption under stand-by conditions. Clock/calendar circuits intended for battery back-up also use CMOS technology, or some other form of micro-power circuit.

A battery back-up circuit is one of those things which seems to be deceptively simple at first. In some cases a very basic circuit of the type shown in Figure 15 will suffice. This uses diodes D1 and D2 to ensure that the battery can not feed power into the mains power supply circuit, and that the latter can not force power into the battery. Both power sources can supply power to the battery backed circuit, but in practice only one or the other will do so. Things must be arranged so that the voltage from the main supply is higher than that provided even by a fresh and fully charged battery. When the main supply is present, it provides power to the circuit, and D1 becomes reverse biased so that it blocks any current flow from the battery. When the main supply is absent, D1 becomes forward biased and supplies power to the circuit, but D2 becomes reverse biased and blocks any current flow into the main supply circuit.

This relies on the battery backed circuit being able to function on a somewhat lower voltage than the main supply potential. A clock/calendar/RAM circuit which is designed to operate on a nominal 5 volt supply will normally be capable of functioning at supply voltages as low as 3 to 3.5 volts, and the

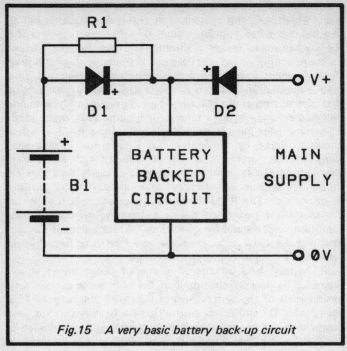

Fig.15 *A very basic battery back-up circuit*

lower voltage from the battery will not normally give any problems. What might produce difficulties is the voltage drop through D2 when the circuit is powered from the main supply. Assuming that an ordinary silicon diode or rectifier is fitted here, the voltage drop will be around 0.65 volts, which will give a significant mismatch between the battery backed circuit and the rest of the system. This can often be sufficient to prevent the battery backed circuit from being accessed properly. A different type of diode, such as a germanium or Schottky type might give a lower voltage drop that would eliminate the problem.

R1 is an optional resistor, and this is only needed if the back-up battery is a nickel-cadmium rechargeable type. The point of including R1 is to provide a trickle charge (usually about 1 or 2 milliamps) to the battery when the main supply

is in operation. Provided the equipment is used for a reasonable length of time at regular intervals, this should keep the
battery fairly well charged, and no other charging should be
necessary. Note though, that the value of R1 must give only a
very low charge current. Otherwise there is a real danger of
the battery becoming over-charged and destroyed. Over-
charging the nickel cadmium batteries can result in them
"gassing", which can in turn lead to the non-vented types
exploding. Recharging any form of primary cell is also a
dubious practice that is probably best avoided.

The ICL7673

In applications where the voltage drop through a diode will
give problems with supply voltage mismatches it is usually
necessary to resort to FET switching devices. These days there
are several integrated circuits available which are designed
specifically for battery back-up control, and which provide
low voltage drop FET switching. The ICL7673 is an example
of such a device, and this has a standard 8 pin DIL package
with the pinout configuration shown in Figure 16. It is used
in the circuit shown in Figure 17.

There are four FETs used as electronic switches in the
ICL7673. Two of these are driven in anti-phase, have one
terminal connected to the earth rail, and the other two terminals available at pins 3 and 6. In most applications these are
not required, and pins 3 and 6 are accordingly left unconnected. They can be used as status outputs if required though.
The other two switches are also driven out-of-phase, and they
each have one terminal connected to pin 1 (the output
terminal). The other side of one switch connects to pin 2,
while the other connects to pin 8. In normal use the battery
supply connects to pin 2 while the main supply connects to
pin 8, and only one supply source will be fed through to the
output. A voltage comparator monitors the two input
voltages, and its output is used to control the two switches.
The circuit is arranged so that the higher of the two voltages
is always connected through to the output. Figure 18 shows
the basic arrangement used in the ICL7673 and should help
to explain the way in which it functions.

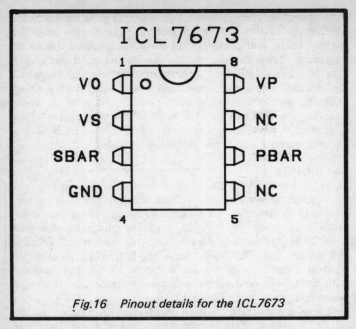

Fig.16   Pinout details for the ICL7673

In common with a simple diode switching circuit, this one relies on the battery supply voltage being significantly lower than the main supply voltage. It also permits trickle charging of a nickel-cadmium back-up battery if required, and this is the purpose of R1 and D1 (which should be omitted if the back-up battery is a primary type).

Where this circuit differs from a diode type is in the amount of voltage drop from the two inputs to the output. Using diode based circuit with silicon devices there is a voltage drop of about 0.65 volts from each input to the output, and this voltage loss is largely independent of the supply current. Field effect transistors used as electronic switches provide what is almost pure resistance, and the voltage drop is therefore dependent on their "on" resistance and the level of current flow. The FET switches in the ICL7673 have a typical "on" resistance of about 30 ohms, and in most cases the supply current being switched will only

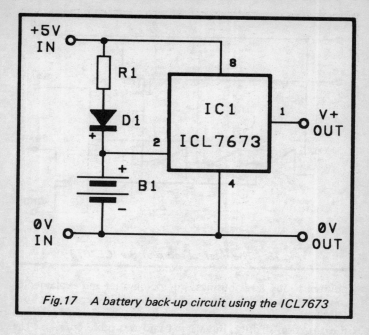

Fig.17   A battery back-up circuit using the ICL7673

be around 50 microamps.   This gives a theoretical voltage drop of only about 1.5 millivolts.

Although the ICL7673 is probably most useful for battery back-up applications that involve a 5 volt main supply and a 3 to 4.5 volt battery voltage, it will function over a 2.5 to 15 volt supply voltage range.   It can also be used at currents of up to 30 milliamps.   For a battery back-up circuit to be practical it must have a low level of current consumption, and this is certainly achieved by the ICL7673 which has a typical quiescent current drain of just 1.5 microamps (5 microamps maximum) with a 3 volt supply.

When designing equipment that utilizes a battery back-up system try to make the equipment fairly easy to setup after the batteries have failed and been replaced.   This also makes it reasonably easy to setup and use the equipment each time it is used in the event of there being a delay in obtaining a new set of batteries.   I recently received stares of disbelief when I

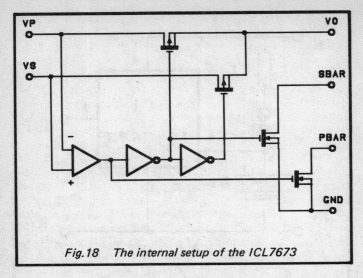

Fig.18   The internal setup of the ICL7673

pointed to my large business microcomputer and explained to some friends that it was currently unusable because its four HP7 batteries had gone flat!   They may have misunderstood the situation slightly, but what I said was quite correct. The contents of the computer's battery backed RAM had become corrupted and were making it difficult to reset everything properly. Battery back-up can easily become a hinderance rather than a help.

An idea that seems to be gaining popularity is to have a battery check circuit that indicates when the batteries are nearing exhaustion. An ultra-high value capacitor (usually 1 farad) is connected in parallel with the back-up battery, and maintains the supply for about 2 minutes when the batteries are removed. This gives ample time to fit the new set of batteries, and avoids the need for any resetting of the clock/calendar/RAM circuits. A battery check circuit is featured at the end of this chapter incidentally.

Adjustable Zener
Zener diodes are the usual choice when a low power shunt regulator circuit is required, but a normal zener diode is not

36

without its drawbacks. The obvious one is that there is no way of varying the zener voltage, and a variable output voltage can only be obtained by using the zener regulator circuit to drive a potentiometer. However, the output impedance of the circuit varies enormously as the output voltage is varied, which can lead to poor performance in some applications. Other drawbacks of zener diodes are their relatively poor temperature stability, and what is generally a rather low standard of regulation performance for types having voltages of about 6.8 volts or less.

The TL430C is an integrated circuit that is intended for use in applications where a zener diode would normally be used, but it offers a couple of advantages. The most important of these is its ability to provide an adjustable output voltage. In addition it provides superior regulation efficiency, including much better temperature stability. The temperature coefficient is actually plus and minus 50 parts per million (PPM) per degree Centigrade.

There are two versions of the TL430C. These are the TL430CJG which has a standard 8 pin DIL plastic package, and the TL430CLP which has a three lead TO-92 (transistor style) encapsulation. Details of both types are shown in Figure 19, but note that the "LP" type is the version which is sold through normal retail outlets. Both are top views, incidentally.

The TL430C is used in the circuit configuration shown in Figure 20. This is essentially the same as a conventional zener shunt regulator circuit with R1 acting as the load resistor. However, IC1 requires two resistors (R2 and R3) to set its operating voltage. The way in which the circuit operates is very similar to a transistor used in the so-called "amplified diode" configuration (see Figure 11 of book BP76). There is normally a very high resistance between the cathode and anode terminals of IC1, but taking the "Ref" terminal above a certain voltage results in the device switching on and this resistance falling to a very low level. The device does not trigger in the same way as a thyristor, and it is a form of linear device (like a transistor) rather than a true switching type. There is only a very small voltage difference between the maximum "off" bias level and the minimum "on" bias

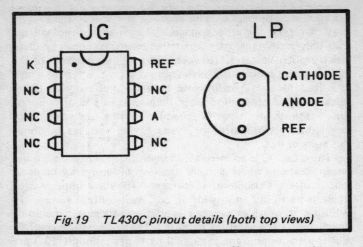

Fig.19   TL430C pinout details (both top views)

voltage. This gives good regulation efficiency, but like an amplified diode circuit, the regulation at low voltages is superior to that at high output voltages.

Although similar to an amplified diode, the mathematics of the TL430C are slightly different. A transistor turns on at a base voltage of around 0.65 volts, but the threshold voltage of the TL430C is much higher at between 2.5 and 3 volts (typically 2.75 volts). This means that the TL430C can not always be used as a replacement for an amplified diode, since the threshold voltage of the device determines the minimum possible regulation voltage. An amplified diode circuit will work down to about 0.65 volts, but the TL430C can not be guaranteed to provide output voltages of less than 3 volts.

The maximum operating voltage of the device is 30 volts. This is the maximum regulated output voltage, and not the highest acceptable unregulated input voltage. As with any shunt regulator, there is no upper limit to the input voltage, but the power dissipated in R1 could be quite high if there is a large input to output voltage differential. The absolute maximum current and power ratings for the TL430C are 100 milliamps and 775 milliwatts respectively. The device is only guaranteed to function properly if it passes a current of more than two milliamps, but in practice it will operate respectably

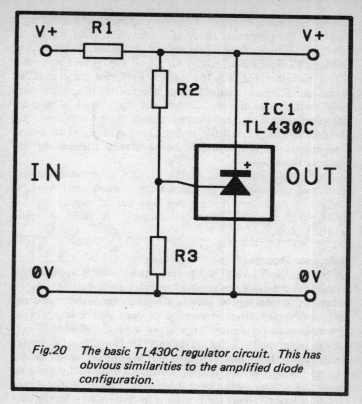

*Fig.20   The basic TL430C regulator circuit. This has
obvious similarities to the amplified diode
configuration.*

well at lower currents.

For the circuit to work efficiently the current flow through
R2 and R3 must be much higher than the current flow into
the "Ref" input of IC1. This input current can be up to 10
microamps. Obviously a very high current through R2 and R3
is undesirable since this would result in a lot of wasted power,
and could result in a high level of power dissipation in R1.
The selected current flow has to be something of a compromise, and a current of about 1 or 2 milliamps will usually give
good results.

With R3 set at 2.7k the current flow is approximately 1
milliamp and the value required for R2 is very easily calculated.

Simply deduct 2.75 volts from the required output voltage, and then the remaining figure is the required value for R2 in kilohms. For instance, if an output potential of 10 volts is needed, 10 minus 2.75 equals 6.25, and the correct value for R2 is therefore 6.25k. The nearest preferred value is 6.2k, which should give adequate accuracy for most applications. This method can not be used to set the output with great precision, and where the output voltage must be spot-on, R2 should be a fixed resistor and a preset connected in series. The output voltage can then be accurately trimmed to the required figure.

The output noise level of the TL430C is somewhat lower than that produced by an average zener diode, but where a really low noise level is required it is still advisable to add a decoupling capacitor across the output. A value of $10\mu F$ is satisfactory.

Reference Sources

Of course, the TL430C is not restricted to use in applications that require a low power shunt regulator. It can be used to provide the reference source in a high power series regulator, and can be fed from a constant current source in order to give improved regulation. It will work very well in this role, giving what will almost invariably be substantially better performance than that provided by an ordinary zener diode. The ability to trim the output voltage to exactly the required figure can also be useful, even in variable voltage circuits where any uncertainty about the precise reference voltage is reflected in the unpredictability of the output voltage range.

The TL430C is just one of many components designed to act as "improved" zener diodes. These highly stable voltage references are invaluable for use in applications where a highly stable supply voltage is required, either when a simple shunt regulator will suffice, or as the basis for a more complex high power supply circuit. One of the best reference voltage devices avilable is the 8069 1.2 volt type. This has a 2 lead TO-18 or TO-92 encapsulation, as detailed in Figure 21. It is used in exactly the same way as a zener diode, but it provides a very high degree of regulation. A variation in current flow of 50 microamps to 5 milliamps (a 100 to 1 span)

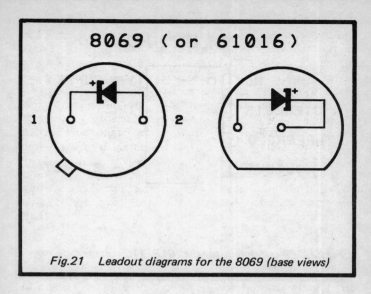

8069 (or 61016)

Fig.21   Leadout diagrams for the 8069 (base views)

produces a change in output voltage of less than 20 millivolts. The temperature coefficient is 0.005% per degree Centigrade. This standard of performance should be sufficient for even the most demanding of applications.

Supply Monitoring
For something like a variable voltage power supply an analogue or digital voltmeter is the normal way of monitoring the output voltage, but this type of thing is a little over-specified for most power supply applications. In most cases there is actually no point in monitoring the supply voltage at all, but it can be helpful to do so in some instances. These are mainly cases where a slight drop in the supply voltage due to a minor fault could go unnoticed, but could have serious consequences. An example of this would be a piece of test gear where a faulty supply could result in erroneous results being obtained, possibly for a considerable period of time, before it became apparent that there was anything amiss.

Voltage monitors are also used a great deal in battery powered equipment where they give warning that the batteries

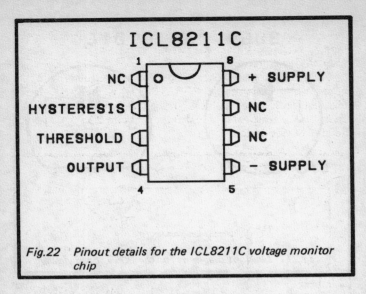

ICL8211C

NC	1	8 + SUPPLY
HYSTERESIS	2	NC
THRESHOLD	3	NC
OUTPUT	4	5 − SUPPLY

Fig.22   Pinout details for the ICL8211C voltage monitor chip

are nearing exhaustion and should be replaced. As explained previously, they can be used to good effect with battery back-up circuits.

It is not particularly difficult to design a circuit that will monitor a supply voltage and light a LED warning indicator if the detected voltage falls below a certain threshold level. It is much more difficult to design a circuit that will do the job really well. The first problem to contend with is the current consumption of the circuit, which must be quite low if the unit is to be a practical proposition in many of its potential applications. It must also have really good accuracy, as the difference between an acceptable supply voltage and one which will give faulty operation is often very restricted. Also, in a battery monitor application the voltage drop as the battery changes from full charge to something nearing exhaustion can be quite low, although this depends to a large degree on the type of battery concerned. Nickel-cadmium cells and other types which have a low internal resistance generally have little voltage variation during their operating lives, whereas ordinary zinc-carbon types produce much wider variations. Another point to bear in mind when designing supply voltage monitors is that they must have good long term stability, and are not very practical if they require frequent recalibration.

There are integrated circuits specifically designed for supply monitor applications, and the ICL8211C is the most readily obtainable of these. It has a very good standard of performance, and is reasonably inexpensive. Figure 22 shows pinout details for this device.

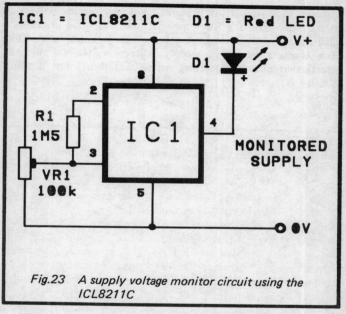

Fig.23   A supply voltage monitor circuit using the ICL8211C

This device consists basically of a voltage comparator and a 1.15 volt reference source. The typical supply current under stand-by conditions is a mere 22 microamps (40 microamps maximum). The action of the device is to switch on a 7 milliamp current sink at its output when the voltage fed to its threshold input drops below 1.15 volts. A LED indicator can therefore be driven direct from its output without the need for a series current limiting resistor. A hysteresis output can be used to provide positive feedback to avoid the circuit "jittering" between the on and off states when the input voltage is close to the 1.15 volt threshold level.

Figure 23 shows the circuit diagram for a supply monitor based on the ICL8211C. VR1 supplies a portion of the supply voltage to the threshold input of IC1, and in practice VR1 is adjusted so that the LED indicator (D1) is switched on when the supply voltage reaches the desired threshold level. R1 provides hysteresis that ensures good stability and an unam biguous indication from the unit. For high supply voltages it is advisable to make R1 somewhat lower in value in order to give sufficient hysteresis. A value of 470k should be suitable. The absolute maximum supply voltage is 30 volts, and the practical minimum operating voltage for the circuit is about 3 volts.

Chapter 2

SWITCH MODE POWER SUPPLIES

From reading some pieces on switch mode power supplies you could gain the impression that they are the only worthwhile form of power supply circuit, and all other types are obsolete. This is far from the truth though, and although switch mode supplies do have definite advantages, they also have their drawbacks. Whether or not they are the best choice for a given application is something that has to be carefully assessed. There are some situations where they are undoubtedly superior to conventional forms of power supply, but in most cases they are totally out of place. The fact most supplies are not of the switching variety demonstrates this fact. Switch mode power supplies are perhaps more common in ready-made equipment (particularly microprocessor and other digital equipment) than they are in designs for the home constructor. Probably the main reason for this is that they are relatively difficult to design, and things can easily end in disaster if the circuit is not quite right. This is something that is true of many types of power supply, but the switch mode variety is that bit more difficult to deal with than other types.

In this chapter we will look at the theory of switch mode power supplies, their advantages, and their disadvantages. We will then consider some simple but versatile practical designs.

Drawbacks

As already pointed out, one drawback of switch mode power supplies is that they are relatively difficult to design, and it is easy to produce a very convincing paper design that fails to work at all in practice. Worse than this, a design that fails to work properly can soon end up with the output device overheating and being destroyed. Errors can also lead to high voltages being generated in the circuit, which can endanger any semiconductor devices present in the design.

Another drawback is that they tend to be more complex than a conventional equivalent. Integrated circuits designed specifically to operate in switch mode power supplies can help to reduce the complexity, but these devices are not amongst the cheapest of integrated circuits. This contrasts with most ordinary regulators which nearly all fall into the low cost category. The cost is also boosted by the need of a high quality inductor or transformer in most types of switch mode supply. From the point of view of the home constructor there is the added problem that suitable ready-made inductors and transformers seem to be unobtainable, and these components therefore need to be home produced. The components needed are not very widely available, but they are stocked by one or two retailers.

Other problems include what is generally a slightly lower level of reliability, and greater difficulty in obtaining a really low noise level on the output. A problem that is often overlooked is the radio frequency interference that is generated by the high frequency switching of the output stage. Obviously this will be irrelevant in many applications, but it makes switch mode supplies a dubious choice for any equipment which is sensitive to radio frequency signals. The radio frequency generation can be contained by careful screening and filtering, but for home constructor projects the effort involved might not be deemed worthwhile by many.

Advantages

The main advantage of switching power supplies is that they are very efficient when compared to ordinary supply circuits. Apart from the low level of wasted power this provides, it has the advantage of giving relatively little heat generation. This avoids the need for massive heatsinks even with designs that provide quite high output powers.

The low level of power dissipation in the output stage is due to the fact that the output transistor is, for the majority of the time, either fully switched on, or fully turned off. When switched off it may well be subjected to quite a high voltage, but as only minute leakage currents will flow, the power dissipation is not significant. When the output transistor is switched on there is a high level of current flow, but the voltage across the device will be quite low. The voltage will still be typically something of the order of one volt, and possibly several times this figure. This is something that is dependent on the particular form of driver and output stage used. However, even at high output currents the power dissipated in the output transistor should still be no more than a few watts, whereas a figure of tens of watts would be more likely with a non-switching type regulator circuit. Also, the output transistor might only be switched on for about 50% of the time, giving an average dissipation figure of only about half the "on" time dissipation. The output transistor will spend some portion of the time making the transition from one state to the other, but this would normally be such a small percentage of the time that it would not significantly affect the power dissipation figure.

Another major attraction of switching supply circuits is their ability to provide a wide range of output voltages from a single input voltage. This can enable a single untapped mains transformer to be used in applications that would otherwise require several transformers and (or) a multi-tapped type. A crucial feature of switch mode supplies is that they remain relatively efficient when transforming supply voltages. With an AC supply a transformer can step the supply voltage up or down, and in theory there is a complementary transformation of the current flow. For example, if an output of 10 volts at 1 amp is taken and the input potential is 20 volts, an input current of 0.5 amps will be drawn. The input and output powers are identical at 10 watts each. With an ordinary series regulator a conversion from 20 to 10 volts is no problem, but with 1 amp output current the input current would have to be at least as high as this. A switch mode power supply can, in theory at any rate, do with DC supplies just what a transformer does with AC supplies. A 20 volt at 0.5 amps to 10 volt at 1 amp conversion is theoretically possible.

In practice neither transformers or switch mode power supplies achieve 100% efficiency, and they may often fall well short of this figure. A switch mode supply will still usually be substantially more efficient than an equivalent series regulator. Another point to bear in mind is that, like a transformer, a switch mode power supply can provide a voltage step-up. This is, of course, quite impossible with an ordinary series regulator. Producing a negative supply from a

47

positive type (or vice versa) is a further very useful ability of switch mode power supplies. This is again something that is beyond the capabilities of conventional power supply circuits.

PWM

Switch mode power supplies rely on pulse width modulation (PWM) as an efficient means of providing a variable output voltage. There are several ways of providing pulse width modulation, but the two most common methods are shown in the block diagrams of Figure 24.

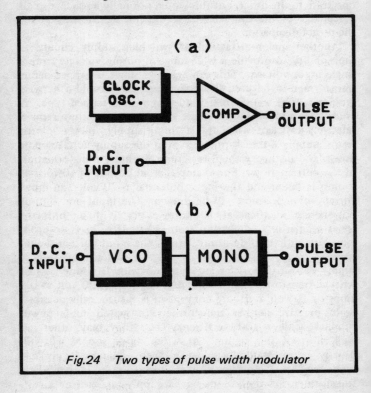

Fig.24   Two types of pulse width modulator

The method shown in Figure 24(a) is the better of the two methods in that it provides an output signal at a constant frequency. The clock oscillator provides a triangular signal. If we assume that the DC input voltage is half way between the peak voltages of the clock signal, the output from the voltage comparator will be a squarewave signal. The waveforms in Figure 25(a) help to explain the way in which this happens. The upper waveform represents the clock signal, and the broken line shows the DC input level. When the input signal is at a lower potential than the clock signal the output of the comparator goes low. When the comparative states of the two signals are reversed, the output of the comparator goes high. This gives the squarewave output signal of the lower waveform. The broken line on this waveform indicates the average output voltage, which is half the supply voltage.

If the input voltage is raised, the mark-space ratio of the output signal is increased, and so is the average output voltage (Figure 25(b)). Decreasing the input voltage gives an output signal with a lower mark-space ratio, and a lower average output voltage (Figure 25(c)).

In the setup of Figure 24(b) a VCO drives a monostable multivibrator, and the input signal is applied to the control input of the VCO. With zero input voltage the VCO fails to oscillate, the monostable is not triggered, and there is zero output voltage. Raising the input voltage brings the VCO into operation, and a series of output pulses are produced by the monostable. The duration of each output pulse is unaffected by the frequency of the VCO. At low frequencies the output pulses are well spread out, and the average output voltage is low. Raising the input voltage further gives a higher VCO frequency, and the pulses from the monostable become bunched closer together. This gives a higher average output voltage, and the required pulse width modulation effect.

This may not seem applicable to a power supply design, where a smooth DC output voltage is required, rather than a pulse signal. However, a lowpass filter at the output is all that is needed to convert the pulse signal to a reasonably smooth DC supply having a potential equal to the average voltage of the pulse signal. This gives the required DC output signal, but leaves the output transistor operating in a switching mode so that it provides good efficiency.

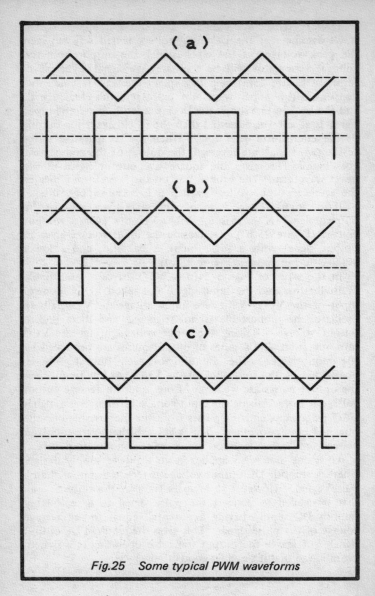

Fig.25   Some typical PWM waveforms

Supply Configuration

A pulse width modulator can easily be merged into conventional power supply circuits. The block diagram of Figure 26 shows the switch mode equivalent of a conventional feedback stabilised supply.

This is no different to an ordinary series regulator circuit in that a reference voltage is fed to the non-inverting input of an error amplifier, and negative feedback is taken to the inverting input by way of a voltage divider circuit. The output is therefore stabilised at some multiple of the reference voltage. As for a conventional circuit of this type, the voltage divider circuit can include a potentiometer if a variable output voltage is required. A buffer amplifier at the output enables high output currents to be supplied if necessary.

Where the unit differs from an ordinary supply is in the addition of a control logic and clock circuit between the output of the error amplifier and the input of the buffer amplifier. The main purpose of this circuit is to provide the pulse width modulation, but it might provide some secondary roles such as output overload protection or thermal shutdown. Note that it is not essential to have a pulse width modulator that will provide an average output voltage that is precisely the same as the DC input voltage. The negative feedback will compensate for any offsets through this circuit and provide the correct output voltage. The error amplifier must be capable of providing a suitable input voltage range for the PWM circuit though, and the modulator must be capable of providing a full range of output voltages. If these criteria are not met the circuit will either fail to function at all, or will have a tendency to latch-up with the output, fully positive or switched off!

A lowpass filter is included at the output to integrate the output pulses into a reasonably smooth DC signal. Note that the feedback must be taken via the lowpass filter.

Output Stages

As described so far a switch mode power supply is only capable of providing an output voltage which is of the same polarity as the input, and at a lower voltage. This is known (for obvious reasons) as a step-down regulator. The same

51

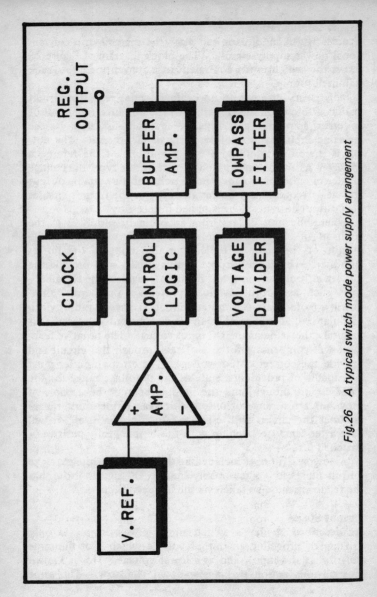

Fig.26 A typical switch mode power supply arrangement

basic configuration can provide a boosted output voltage, or one of the opposite polarity to the input supply. All that is needed is some revamping of the output and filter stages in order to give the desired type of output. These other modes of operation will probably be easier to understand if we first take a closer look at the step-down output stage and filter configuration. The basic step-down output circuit is as shown in Figure 27. This type of switch mode output stage is sometimes referred to by its American "buck" name incidentally.

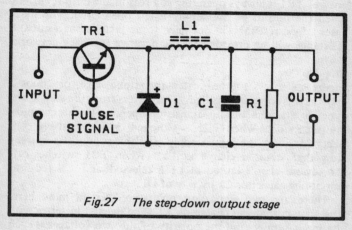

Fig.27   The step-down output stage

TR1 is an emitter follower stage, which is, of course, used as an electronic switch in this application. The voltage at its emitter rises to virtually the full input supply voltage when TR1 is switched on, which gives a voltage across L1 that is almost equal to the difference between the input and output voltages. Accordingly, the current flow through L1 and into C1 steadily rises, and this process continues until TR1 switches off. L1 stores up an electrical charge during TR1's "on" period, and this charge is released when TR1 is switched off. This charge is produced by the collapsing magnetic field around the inductor, and it is of reverse polarity to the signal originally fed into L1. It is coupled into C1 via D1. When TR1 switches on again a charge current flows through L1 and into C1 once more, L1 charges C1 when TR1 switches off

53

again, and so on.

The action of the circuit is really just that of a standard L-C lowpass filter, and provided C1 and L1 are quite high in value in relation to the input frequency and output load impedance, a reasonably well smoothed DC output will be obtained. D1 is needed merely because of the non-symmetrical nature of the output stage. A complementary emitter follower output stage could be used, but it is cheaper to use a diode instead of another output transistor. R1 is a load resistor which ensures TR1 is always operating at a reasonable output current when the output of the supply is left open circuit. In most cases a load resistor will not need to be included as a suitable resistance will be provided by the negative feedback network.

Step-Up Circuit

Figure 28 shows the basic step-up output stage, or "boost" stage as it is sometimes called. This differs from the step-down type in that the output transistor operates in the common emitter mode. When TR1 is switched on it effectively connects L1 across the input supply, and this produces a current flow that stores a charge in L1. When TR1 switches off, the reverse charge stored in L1 is released, and it is fed into smoothing capacitor C1 by way of D1.

There are two important points to keep in mind here. The first is that the charge on L1 is connected in series with the input supply, and the polarity of the two voltages is such that they are added together. This gives an output voltage that is greater than the input supply voltage. The other important point is that the voltage produced across L1 as it discharges can be many times greater than the input supply voltage. This configuration is not, therefore, restricted to voltage doubling, but can be used to provide substantial voltage boosts. However, this is very much dependent on the inductor used for L1 having suitable qualities. When TR1 is switched on, L1 and TR1 are virtually short circuiting the input supply, and this could have disastrous consequences if the properties of L1 are unsuitable. For satisfactory results it is usually necessary to have a high Q inductor wound on a ferrite potcore.

D1 is an important part of the circuit. It ensures that when

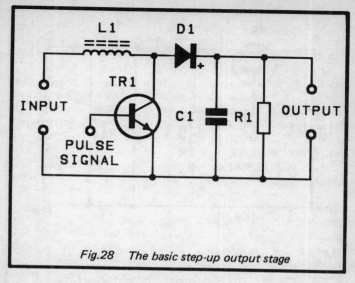

Fig.28   The basic step-up output stage

TR1 is switched on it does not short circuit C1 and cut off the output. R1 is again a load resistor, and without this component and no load connected across the output the output voltage will tend to drift to a high voltage. Normally this resistance will be provided by the negative feedback circuit, but proper regulation of the output is not possible without at least a low power load connected across the output of the supply.

Inverter

A switch mode power supply circuit that provides conversion from a positive supply to a negative type (or vice versa) is called an "inverter" circuit, or the American "buck-boost" name is sometimes used. The latter is a reasonably apt name, as I suppose this configuration has features in common with both the "buck" (step-down) and "boost" (step-up) types. Figure 29 shows the basic inverter output stage circuit.

This configuration is similar to the step-down type in that it uses an emitter follower output transistor, but it drives an inductor when it is switched on, as in the step-up configuration.

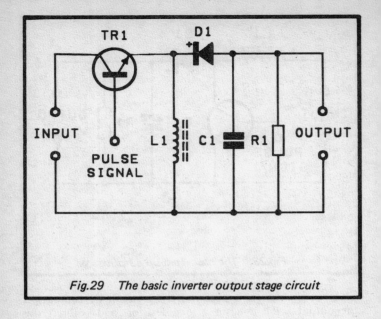

Fig.29   The basic inverter output stage circuit

This setup is different to the step-up type though, as one side of the inductor (L1) is connected to earth. When TR1 switches off, L1 gives up its reverse charge, and this signal is fed via D1 to smoothing capacitor C1. The circuit therefore generates a series of negative output pulses that produce a smoothed negative output voltage on C1. D1 prevents TR1 feeding a positive pulse to C1 each time TR1 switches on.

We are assuming here that the input supply is a positive type, and that the output is negative, but an inversion in the opposite direction can be achieved by using a PNP device for TR1 and reversing the polarity of D1. Note that the voltage pulses developed across L1 can be much higher than the input voltage, and that this configuration can therefore provide a voltage boost as well as a change in polarity.

There are actually many more types of switch mode supply output stages than the three basic types described here, but the others are really just variations on these three types. These three standard configurations are sufficient to satisfy all normal requirements.

The TL497

There are a great many switch mode power supply integrated circuits available, from simple low power types designed to give a 9 volt output from a single 1.5 volt cell, through to high power types intended for operation in a number of operating modes. They represent an interesting area of electronics for the experimenter, but switch mode power supplies are not as simple and straightforward as most other types of power supply circuit. Of the switch mode integrated circuits I have used the TL497 has always proved to be relatively easy to use and reliable in operation. It does not offer the last word in performance, but it is a functional device that is well suited to use in projects for the home constructor. The TL497 has a standard 14 pin DIL plastic package, and the pinout configuration is shown in Figure 30. The block diagram of Figure 31 shows the internal arrangement used in this device.

Starting with the output stage, there is an NPN output transistor which has both the emitter and the collector terminals left unconnected. This enables the output transistor to be connected to operate as an emitter follower or a common emitter amplifier. It can therefore operate in any normal type of switch mode output stage. There is also a rectifier which has both terminals left unconnected so that it can be used in any standard form of output stage. Note though, that the use of a discrete rectifier is recommended if the TL497 is operated as an inverter type supply. Obviously in the inverter mode the rectifier would be taken several volts negative of the 0 volt supply rail, and this would presumably give problems with parasitic transistors (and possibly the destruction of the device).

The internal reference generator is a 1.2 volt type, but the actual reference voltage can be anything from 1.08 volts to 1.32 volts (i.e. a tolerance of 10%). This voltage is coupled internally to the non-inverting input of a voltage comparator, and it is not available externally. The comparator performs much the same task as the error amplifier in a conventional power supply circuit, and negative feedback to its inverting

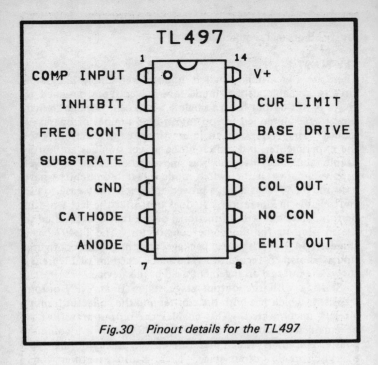

Fig.30   Pinout details for the TL497

input is used to regulate the output voltage. The TL497 functions in a way that is rather more simple than the system outlined previously, and it operates in a manner which is rather reminiscent of a relaxation oscillator. The output of the comparator controls an oscillator, and if the voltage fed to the comparator via the feedback network falls below the reference voltage, the oscillator is activated. If the potential fed to the comparator goes higher than the reference voltage, the oscillator is disabled.

This does not give a conventional pulse width modulation output signal. The output voltage is regulated by bursts of oscillation being used to top-up the smoothing capacitor each time its charge potential falls below a certain threshold level, but the oscillation is cut off as soon as the output voltage is brought up marginally above this threshold level. The output

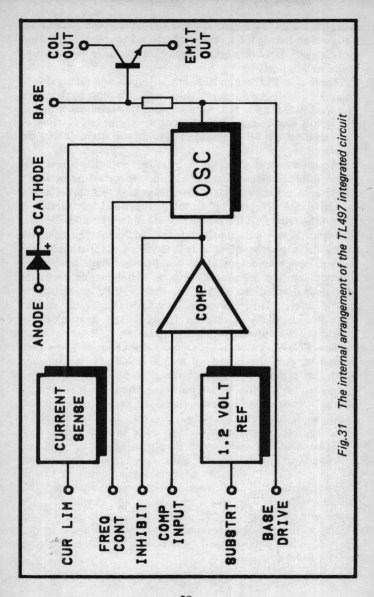

Fig.31   The internal arrangement of the TL497 integrated circuit

signal is bursts of oscillation which are pulse width modulated, rather than having the modulation applied to individual output pulses. This is a fairly crude way of doing things, but it works quite well in practice.

There is a TTL compatible inhibit input, and taking this to logic 1 cuts off the output of the supply. In most applications the inhibit facility is not required, and this terminal is tied to the 0 volt supply rail (it should not simply be left floating, as this method almost certainly result in the device being de-activated.)

A current sensing circuit is included, and this forms part of an output current limiting circuit. It would be perfectly possible to use conventional current limiting techniques with a switch mode power supply, but an overload circuit that is fully integrated into the design is preferable. With conventional forms of current limiting circuit, including the foldback type, there can be quite a high level of dissipation in the output device under overload conditions. With the output current limiting integrated into a switch mode regulator the dissipation in the output transistor can be kept down to a low level. This will often be important, as the output transistor is likely to have relatively little heatsinking in relation to the output powers involved.

The TL497 is not a high power device, and it can only handle output currents of up to 500 milliamps (less in some modes of operation). It can be used with an external power transistor to provide higher output currents, but in general, things become much more critical if switch mode power supplies are used at high output powers. Greater care therefore needs to be exercised if the device is used in this way.

Some switch mode power supply integrated circuits are restricted to operation at quite low input and output voltages. The TL497 has reasonable performance in this respect, particularly with regard to the maximum acceptable output voltage. The actual maximums are 15 volts for the input and 30 volts for the output. However, the 15 volt figure is an absolute maximum, and the maximum recommended input potential is 12 volts. The minimum operating voltage is 4.5 volts.

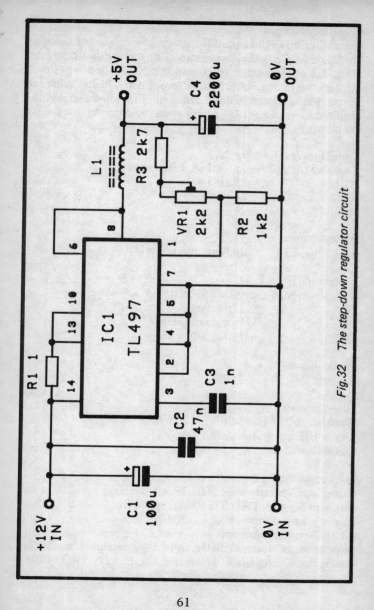

Fig.32   The step-down regulator circuit

Step-Down Circuit

Figure 32 shows the circuit for a step-down regulator based on the TL497. C3 is the timing capacitor for the oscillator, and R1 is the discrete sense resistor in the current limiting circuit. R1 sets the limit level at 500 milliamps, but a higher value can be used if a lower limit is required. Dividing 0.5 by the required limit current (in amps) gives the correct value for R1 (in ohms).

Components for Figure 32
Resistors (All 0.25W 5% carbon unless noted)
R1	1R (0.5W)
R2	1k2
R3	2k7

Potentiometer
VR1	2k2 sub-min preset

Capacitors
C1	100µ 25V elect
C2	47n ceramic
C3	1n polyester layer
C4	2200µ 10V elect

Semiconductor
IC1	TL497

Miscellaneous
Materials for L1 (see below)
14 pin DIL integrated circuit holder
Circuit board, etc.

Parts required for L1
Pair of RM6 potcores (B65807 JR30)
Former (B65808 A1003D2 RM6)
Pair of clamps (B65808 A2203 RM6)
24 SWG enamelled copper wire
(All these parts are available from Electrovalue Ltd., 28 St. Judes Road, Englefield Green, Egham, Surrey, TW20 0HB.)

C1 and C2 are smoothing and decoupling capacitors at the input. Due to the pulsed nature of the input supply it is advisable to have decoupling capacitors mounted close to IC1, even if the source supply is well smoothed. C4 is the smoothing capacitor at the output, and L1 is the inductive element of the lowpass filter. R2, R3, and VR1 are the negative feedback network, and they are designed for a 5 volt output. However, VR1 enables other output voltages to be obtained, and the feedback network can be redesigned to accommodate output voltages that do not fall within the present confines of VR1. The minimum output voltage is about 1.2 volts, which is imposed by the internal reference voltage. The supply is a bit pointless with voltages of much more than about 6 volts, as it would then offer no greater efficiency than a conventional series regulator circuit.

The prototype provided a reasonable level of performance under test, and was found to have an input current of approximately 250 milliamps with an output current of 400 milliamps. This represents an input power of 3 watts (12V x 0.25A = 3 watts), and an output power of 2 watts (5V x 0.4A = 2 watts). In terms of efficiency, this is clearly 66.66%, which compares favourably with a conventional series regulator. This would require an input current of at least 400 milliamps, which gives an input power of 4.8 watts for 2 watts out. This represents a maximum possible efficiency of 41.66%, and in practice the efficiency obtained would probably be significantly lower than this. This step-down regulator is therefore almost twice as efficient as a typical series regulator would be under the same operating conditions.

Step-Up Circuit

The circuit diagram for a step-up regulator based on the TL497 is provided in Figure 33. This is similar to the step-down circuit, but the output stage has been revamped into the standard step-up configuration. Although the circuit is designed to give a 12 volt output from a 5 volt input, it should work properly with other input and output voltages within the operating range of the TL497. Of course, the values in the feedback network (R2, R3, and VR1) will need to be altered in order to accommodate output voltages that are well

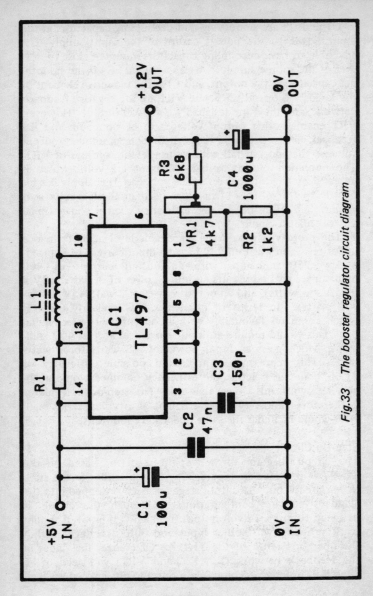

Fig.33   The booster regulator circuit diagram

64

removed from the present 12 volt output level. Also, bear in mind that only a very limited maximum output current will be available if a large step-up in voltage is provided by the circuit.

Components for Figure 33
Resistors (All 0.25W 5% carbon unless noted)
R1	1R (0.5W)
R2	1k2
R3	6k8

Potentiometer
VR1	4k7 sub-min preset

Capacitors
C1	100μ 25V elect
C2	47n ceramic
C3	150p polystyrene
C4	1000μ 25V elect

Semiconductor
IC1	TL497

Miscellaneous
Materials for L1 (see below)
14 pin DIL integrated circuit holder
Circuit board, etc.

Parts required for L1
Pair of RM8 potcores (B65811 JR41)
Former (B65812 A1005D1 RM8)
Pair of clamps (B65812 A2203 RM6)
22 SWG enamelled copper wire
(All these parts are available from Electrovalue Ltd., 28 St. Judes Road, Englefield Green, Egham, Surrey TW20 0HB.)

The performance of the step-up circuit is quite good, with an input current of about 550 milliamps being drawn with an output current of 150 milliamps. This represents an input power of 2.75 watts to give an output power of

1.8 watts, or an efficiency of 65.45%. No direct comparison with a conventional series regulator is possible in this case since a voltage step-up is impossible with an ordinary series regulator. A step-up circuit of this type would normally be used where the main circuit requires (say) a 5 volt supply at a fairly high current, plus a higher voltage supply at a much lower current. The step-up circuit may offer a cheaper and neater solution than providing a separate mains supply to provide the higher voltage.

An inverter circuit based on the TL497 is shown in Figure 34. This is similar to the two previous circuits, but the output stage has been modified into the standard inverter type. As explained previously, the internal diode of the TL497 should not be used in this mode, and external rectifier D1 has therefore been used instead. The negative feedback circuit has also been modified slightly. This is because the substrate terminal (pin 4) has been connected to the −5 volt output of the circuit. The 1.2 volt reference level is consequently 1.2 volts positive of the −5 volt output, and not 1.2 volts above the 0 volt output. As far as the negative feedback action is concerned, this effectively makes the −5 volt output the earth rail and the 0 volt rail the output that is being stabilised. This may seem to be a rather topsy-turvey way of doing things, but it is the only way that the TL497 can operate in the inverter mode, and it works well in practice. Although the circuit has been designed to give a −5 volt supply from a +5 volt type, once again, it can operate with other input voltages and provide different output voltages. The obvious proviso is that the input and output voltages must be within the safe operating range of the TL497, and where necessary, slight modifications must be made to the negative feedback network.

In terms of efficiency, this circuit required an input current of approximately 240 milliamps in order to provide an output current of 100 milliamps. The maximum available output current before the output voltage started to show signs of loading downwards was about 180 milliamps. This does not represent a very high level of efficiency, and the circuit is actually less than 50% efficient. Results with a 12 volt input were slightly better, but not massively so.

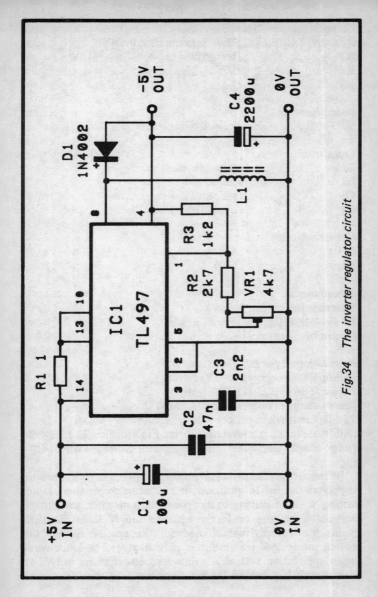

Fig.34   The inverter regulator circuit

Components for Figure 34
Resistors (All 0.25W 5% carbon unless noted)
R1   1R (0.5W)
R2   2k7
R3   1k2

Potentiometer
VR1   4k7 sub-min preset

Capacitors
C1   100µ 25V elect
C2   47n ceramic
C3   2n2 polyester layer
C4   2200µ 10V elect

Semiconductors
IC1   TL497
D1   1N4002

Miscellaneous
Materials for L1 (see below)
14 pin DIL integrated circuit holder
Circuit board, etc.

Parts required for L1
Pair of RM8 potcores (B65811 JR41)
Former (B65812 A1005D1 RM8)
Pair of clamps (B65812 A2203 RM8)
22 SWG enamelled copper wire
(All these parts are available from Electrovalue Ltd., 28 St.
Judes Road, Englefield Green, Egham, Surrey TW20 0HB.)

When designing a mains power supply where a negative
supply is needed in addition to a positive type, there is not
normally any difficulty in incorporating a rectifier, smoothing,
and regulator to provide the negative supply from the same
mains transformer that is used for the positive supply. A
switch mode inverter circuit is only likely to be worthwhile
in an application such as a computer add-on where only a +5
volt output is provided by the computer port, but the add-on

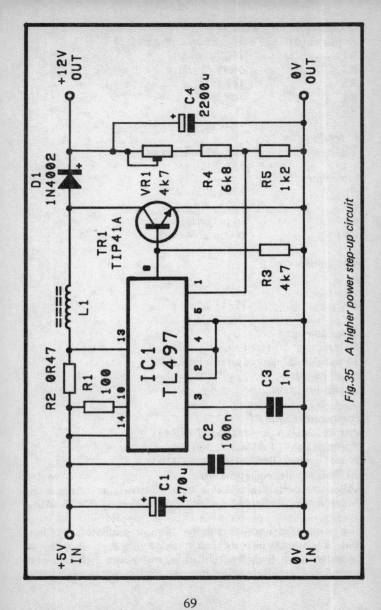

Fig.35   A higher power step-up circuit

69

Components for Figure 35
Resistors (All 0.25W 5% carbon unless noted)
R1   100
R2   0R47 (2 watt)
R3   4k7
R4   6k8
R6   1k2

Potentiometer
VR1   4k7 sub-min preset

Capacitors
C1   470μ 25V elect
C2   100n ceramic
C3   1n polyester layer
C4   2000μ 25V elect

Semiconductors
IC1   TL497
D1   1N4002
TR1   TIP41A

Miscellaneous
Materials for L1 (see below)
14 pin DIL integrated circuit holder
Small heatsink
Circuit board, etc.

Parts required for L1
Pair of RM10 potcores (B65813 JR41)
Former (B65814 A1008D1 RM10)
Pair of clamps (B65814 A2203 RM10)
20 SWG enamelled copper wire
(All these parts are available from Electrovalue Ltd., 28 St. Judes Road, Englefield Green, Egham, Surrey TW20 0HB.)

also requires a negative supply. Simple oscillator, rectifier, and smoothing circuits can provide negative supplies at currents of up to a few milliamps, but where higher powers are needed a switch mode inverter circuit represents what is likely to be the only practical solution to the problem. A slight lack of efficiency is then only a minor price to pay.

Higher Power

As mentioned previously, the TL497 can be used to handle higher powers with the aid of an external output transistor. Figure 35 shows the circuit diagram for a step-up regulator that makes use of this technique. The output stage is still a fairly standard step-up type, but it has external rectifier D1 because the higher current levels can not be handled by the internal rectifier. TR1 is the external switching transistor, and this operates in the common emitter mode. It is driven by the internal switching transistor of IC1 which operates in the emitter follower mode. R1 provides current limiting to protect TR1 against an excessive base current. R2 is the current sense resistor, and this has a value which enables input currents of a little over 1 amp to be handled.

The performance of this circuit is in line with the low power version, but it can handle maximum input and output currents about twice as high as the lower power circuit.

Inductors

For these circuits to operate properly it is imperative that the inductors are of a suitable value and type. Unfortunately, suitable ready-made components do not seem to be available. On the other hand, the components needed for do-it-yourself versions can be obtained, and putting together a suitable component is not very difficult. For the step-down circuit a pair of RM6 potcores are required (they are normally only sold as pairs). "Core" is perhaps a slightly misleading name, as these fit around the winding as well as inside it. The coil is wound on a bobbin designed to fit this size of core, and the winding consists of as many turns of 24 SWG enamelled copper wire as can be accommodated by the bobbin. Try to make the winding reasonably neat, and be sure to wind it tightly. Bear in mind that the winding must not be allowed to protrude above the top and bottom cheeks of the former, or it will be impossible to fit it into the potcore. Leave two lead-out wires about 20 millimetres in length. Scrape the insulation from these using a knife or miniature file, and then tin them

71

with solder.

The bobbin can then be fitted inside the potcore. Two clamps are used to hold the top and bottom sections of the potcore together, and these should be carefully clipped into place. The ferrite material from which potcores are constructed is very hard and brittle, and the cores need to be treated with respect. Dropping them onto something hard from a height of about half a metre or more is quite likely to result in them smashing into several pieces. Be careful not to knock them off the workbench and onto a floor with a hard covering. The bobbin is fitted with printed circuit pins, and each leadout wire is trimmed to length and soldered to one of these. Which two pins you use is entirely up to you, but it is probably best to choose two on opposite sides of the former. Note that there are slits in the bottom cheek of the bobbin, plus matching cutouts in the potcore, which enable the leadout wires to be easily brought out through the base of the potcore assembly.

Figure 36 should help to clarify the way in which everything fits together if you are not familiar with potcores. Quite frankly, once you actually have the components it is pretty obvious how everything fits together.

I failed to get good results with the step-up and inverter circuits using an RM6 size core, but the slightly larger RM8 type proved to be satisfactory. Results were actually marginally better using an RM10 type, but were not really sufficiently improved to justify the use of this much larger size core.

The coils for the step-up and inverter circuits are the same, and are constructed in much the same way as the inductor in the step-down circuit. The winding consists of 26 ½ turns of 22 SWG enamelled copper wire.

Due to the higher currents involved in the higher power version of the step-up circuit, a heavier gauge of wire must be used, and in order to accommodate this an RM10 potcore is required. The winding consists of 1.5 metres of 20 SWG enamelled copper wire wound as neatly and as tightly as possible onto the former.

The components list for these four circuits give full details of the constituent parts for the inductors, and the use of alternative potcore components is not recommended.

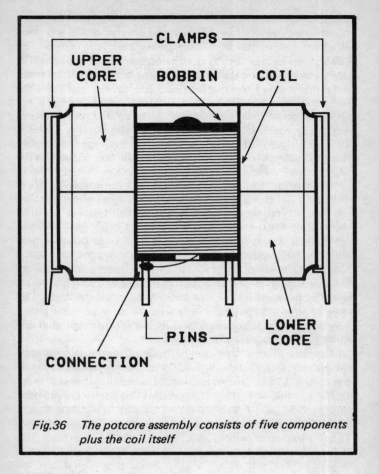

CLAMPS

UPPER CORE **BOBBIN** **COIL**

PINS

LOWER CORE

CONNECTION

Fig.36   The potcore assembly consists of five components plus the coil itself

Other Types

The switch mode power supplies described so far are examples of just one genre, and there are several other types. Many of the switch mode power supplies used in commercial equipment are of the type where the mains supply is rectified and smoothed, and then "chopped" at a high frequency. This high frequency signal is coupled to a step-down and isolation transformers in the normal way. The difference is in the transformer which can be physically very small and very efficient due to the high frequencies involved. Quite high powers can be handled by a transformer wound on an RM10 size potcore, but designing and building a suitable transformer is far from easy. Apart from the dire consequences for the components in the circuit if a mistake is made, there is the problem of adequate insulation between the primary and secondary windings. The small size of the potcore makes it difficult to get really effective insulation between the primary and secondary windings. It is not only the components in the supply circuit that are at risk if this insulation should prove to be inadequate, and anyone using the equipment would be in danger of receiving a severe electric shock. These "offline switcher" type power supplies are probably not a practical proposition for the majority of electronics hobbyists.

There is a very simple type of switch mode power supply which is well suited to home constructor designs, and this is a form of inverter supply. It differs from a conventional inverter supply in that it does not require an inductor, and it operates on what is really an entirely different principle. This type of supply is generally only used where a very low power negative supply is required, and high levels of regulation and noise performance are not required.

Supplies of this type can be built up using discrete component circuits, but in practice it is usually much easier to use the ICL7660 integrated circuit which is designed specifically for this task. Pinout details for this device are provided in Figure 37, and Figure 38 shows the way in which it is used. The ICL7660 is basically just an audio oscillator driving a DPDT electronic switch, and Figure 39 helps to explain how this setup is used to generate a negative supply from a positive input.

C1 is used to transfer power from the input supply to the output supply rails, and C2 provides smoothing at the output. Initially, with the switch in the position shown in Figure 39, C1 is charged up by the input supply. When the electronic switch (S1) is set to the opposite position, C1 is discharged into the output circuit and smoothing capacitor C2. The important point to note here is that the polarity of C1 is such

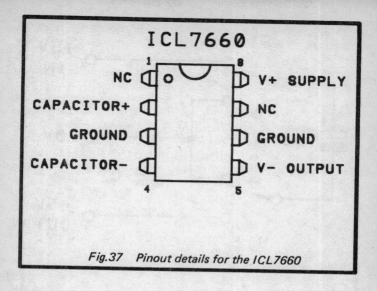

Fig.37   Pinout details for the ICL7660

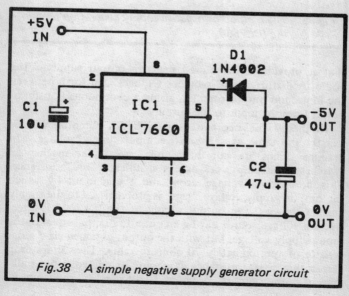

Fig.38   A simple negative supply generator circuit

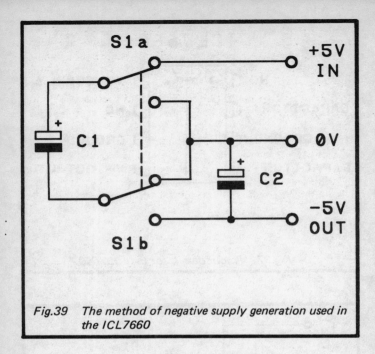

Fig.39   The method of negative supply generation used in
         the ICL7660

that it provides the required negative output supply. The audio oscillator rapidly switches C1 back and forth between the input and output supplies, giving a continuous transfer of power from the input to the output.

In theory the negative output supply potential will be exactly the same as the positive input supply voltage. In practice things are not this simple, and unlike mechanical switches, electronic types have a significant "on" resistance. This produces a voltage drop, and the amount by which the output supply voltage "sags" is proportional to the supply current drawn. The output supply of the ICL7660 is effectively a voltage source having an output potential equal to the input supply voltage, but with the output obtained via a series resistor of approximately 70 ohms in value. The voltage drop across this series resistance is about 70 millivolts per milli-amp of output current, or about 1 volt per 14.2 milliamps of

76

output current to look at it another way. This lack of output current capability, absence of output voltage regulation, plus the fairly high noise level on the output, renders the circuit totally unsitable for many applications. On the other hand, there is a surprisingly large number of occasions when the ICL7660 proves to be just about ideal, and it is to be found in a large number of home constructor and commercial designs.

If we return to the circuit of Figure 38, C1 and C2 are the equivalents to C1 and C2 of Figure 39. The connection from pin 6 to the 0 volt supply rail is shown as a broken line as it is only required for supply voltages below 3.5 volts. Similarly, D1 is only needed for supply voltages of more than 6.5 volts, and with lower supply voltages it should simply be replaced with a link wire.

The circuit will operate over a supply voltage range of 1.5 to 10 volts (provided the provisions mentioned above are observed). The output current should not exceed 40 milliamps, and the maximum permissible dissipation in IC1 is 300 milliwatts. The supply current drawn by IC1 is approximately 170 microamps, but the current drawn from the negative supply rail must be added to this to give the total current drain on the input supply.

Chapter 3

COMPUTER CONTROLLED SUPPLIES

A conventional variable voltage power supply has a potentiometer with a calibrated scale so that the desired output voltage
can be set with reasonable accuracy. In theory this enables
any output within the operating limits of the supply to be set,
but in practice the potentiometer will not have infinite resolution. It should, nevertheless, have sufficient resolution to
permit any desired voltage (within reason) to be set accurately.
The only slight flaw with this type of supply is that the
accuracy with which voltages can be set is often not very good.
This is due partly to the inevitable calibration errors, but is
mainly a result of the limited accuracy of a simple pointer
knob and scale. A built-in voltmeter offers better setting
accuracy, but for really accurate results a digital type having a
minimum of three digits is required. Accuracy should not
then be a problem, but setting the required output voltage
may well be a rather fiddly task.

An approach adopted in some modern power supplies is to
have a digital voltage selector system. This gives a finite
resolution, and what in practice may be only a fairly limited
number of output voltages. It has the advantage that the
desired output voltage, provided it is within the repertoire
of the power supply circuit, can be almost instantly dialled
up, keyed in, or whatever. Provided the system has been set
up correctly, any selected output voltage should be obtained
with a high degree of accuracy.

Apart from being able to quickly set desired voltages,
digital systems can offer facilities that are beyond the scope
of conventional supplies. These facilities are mainly concerned
with automatic testing, and would normally be accomplished
with the aid of a home computer or some other form of
microprocessor controller. The type of thing we are talking
about here is where the supply voltage to a piece of equipment
is varied over a range of voltages while the performance of the
equipment is monitored. This sort of job can be very time
consuming when everything has to be done manually, but

with a fully automated system it will often take only a few seconds for a series of tests to be completed.

This type of testing was once restricted to well financed commercial research and testing laboratories. These days it is well within the reach of hobbyists who own a suitable home computer. A home computer which is equipped with suitable input and output ports is ideal for this type of testing (the BBC computers being obvious candidates for applications of this type). BASIC programs are usually quite fast enough for this type of testing, and in many cases a suitable program with perhaps only a couple of dozens lines can be quickly devised. A home computer provides a degree of sophistication and versatility that is difficult to achieve with a custom built micro-controller unit!

Switched Voltages
In this chapter we will consider some simple methods of digital control for power supplies, but before moving on to these it would be as well to consider a simple alternative. If a few switched output voltages are all that is required, a digital control circuit of some kind is not really justified. All that is really needed is a few switched resistors in the negative feedback network of a conventional power supply design. This method is outlined in the skeleton circuit of Figure 40.

There are actually numerous similar approaches to providing switched output voltages, but this method is perhaps the most practical. The use of preset resistors rather than (say) a potential divider chain of fixed value close tolerance resistors, enables any output voltages within the range of the supply to be obtained with a high degree of precision. With fixed value resistors the restrictions of preferred values might be such that there is no way of obtaining all the desired voltages without resorting to a very complex resistor network.

Digital Control
Although the circuit of Figure 40 provides only five switched output potentials, this system is perfectly suitable for applications where about a dozen or less output voltages are needed. It is just a matter of using a switch with the appropriate number of ways, with a different preset being switched into

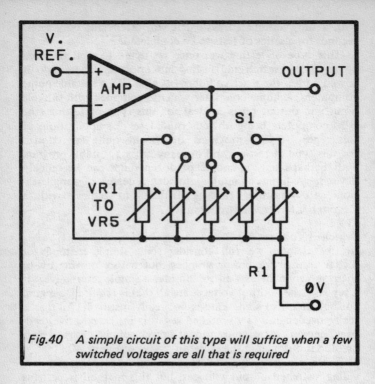

Fig.40 *A simple circuit of this type will suffice when a few switched voltages are all that is required*

circuit at each position. This system becomes a little impractical for larger numbers of output voltages, mainly because a switch having a large enough number of positions is unlikely to be obtainable. There is the additional problem that with a large number of output voltages (which in practice could be over one hundred) the use of a separate preset to control each output voltage becomes impractical. Even if a series of fixed value resistors could be used, it would still be a rather cumbersome way of doing things. Some form of digital control offers a much more practical solution, and need not be highly complex or expensive.

Figure 41 shows a very simple means of providing digital control on a conventional power supply circuit. This is applicable to any "four terminal" style regulator, including

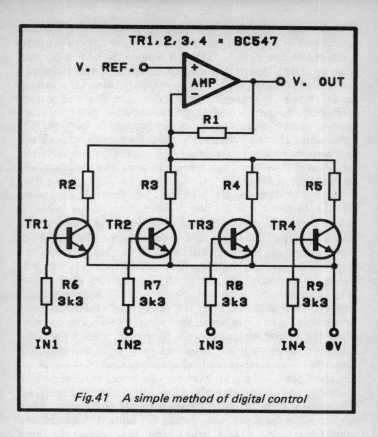

Fig.41   A simple method of digital control

the L200. In its most basic form the circuit has a switching transistor and shunt resistor for each output voltage that is required, and the shunt resistors can be preset types if necessary. Taking the appropriate input to logic 1 switches on one of the transistors and connects the required shunt resistor into circuit. This method is quite versatile in that it enables any desired output voltages to be obtained, but it is inconvenient in that a large number of digital input lines are needed in order to obtain a reasonable number of output voltages (a separate input line being needed for each output voltage).

Although only four switching transistors and shunt resistors are shown in Figure 41, virtually any number of these can be included in the circuit. There is a limit to the number that can be used, because the leakage currents of the transistors are added together, and with too many transistors this leakage could make it impossible to obtain the required output voltages. However, the leakage current of a BC547 (or any similar silicon transistor) is typically only a fraction of a microamp, and the current through the feedback network will presumably be a few milliamps. Consequently there should be no trouble if as many as a few dozen switching transistors and shunt resistors are used.

One way of easing the problem of finding sufficient input lines is to add a 4 to 16 line decoder ahead of the switching transistors. A device of this type has four binary input terminals plus 16 outputs, and under static conditions one of these outputs is always at logic 1. With four inputs the binary input value can be anything from 0000 to 1111, which in terms of ordinary decimal numbering equates to 0 to 15. The outputs are numbered "0" to "15", and applying a binary value to the input of the device sends the appropriate output to logic 1. In actual fact some 4 to 16 line decoders have the output normally in the high state, with the selected output line going low. These can only drive the circuit of Figure 41 if an inverter is added at each output.

The CMOS 4514 is an example of a device with active high outputs, and it can directly drive the circuit of Figure 41. Figure 42 gives pinout details for this component while Figure 43 gives connection details for using it in the present application. Pin 1 is a strobe input that latches the input data on a high to low transition. It is assumed here that the inputs are driven from latching outputs, and that this pin can therefore be tied to logic 1 so that the latches become "transparent". It might be possible to use this device direct onto the data bus of a microprocessor system with strobe pulses from the address decoder being applied to pin 1, but CMOS integrated circuits are by no means compatible with all microprocessors. Pin 23 is an inhibit input, and when taken high this switches off all the outputs. This facility will presumably not be needed in this application, and so pin 23 is

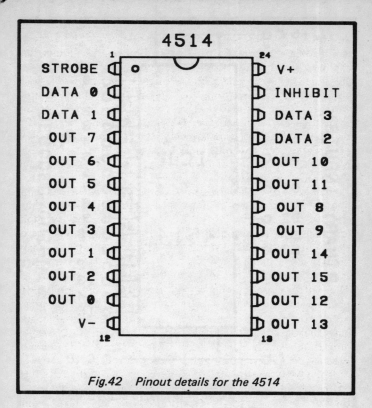

Fig.42   Pinout details for the 4514

connected to the 0 volt supply rail.

D/A Conversion
A much more simple way of obtaining more output voltages
for a given number of input lines is to activate more than one
transistor at a time. This is more restrictive in that it does not
permit any desired output voltages to be obtained, and in
practice it can be difficult to obtain usable results. With a
circuit of this type the output voltages tend to be odd
amounts when more than one transistor is activated. Better
results can be obtained by using a circuit based on an
inverting amplifier, and standard linear digital to analogue

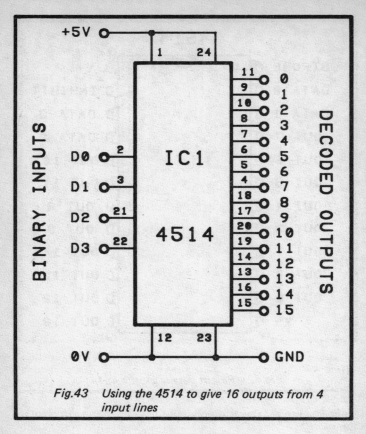

Fig.43 *Using the 4514 to give 16 outputs from 4 input lines*

conversion can then be provided by the circuit. However, where a large number of output voltages are required it is probably better to resort to a proper digital to analogue converter. Some current devices are reasonably inexpensive, but offer a very high level of performance. An attractive feature of many digital to analogue converter chips from the point of view of power supply applications is their high quality built-in reference voltage sources. These often offer true voltage reference performance, and compared to zener diodes have vastly superior accuracy and stability.

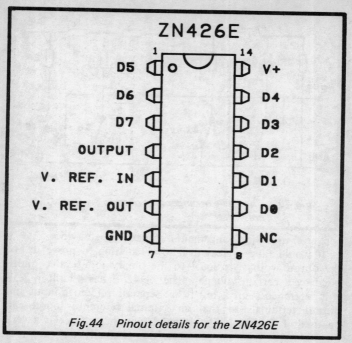

Fig.44   Pinout details for the ZN426E

The ZN426E is a digital to analogue converter chip that offers good performance at reasonable cost. It includes a high quality 2.55 volt reference voltage source. Figure 44 shows pinout details for the ZN426E.

It is an eight bit device, and therefore has eight digital inputs ("D0" to "D7"). These data inputs are compatible with TTL logic devices, as well as CMOS circuits that are powered from a 5 volt supply. The ZN426E also seems to work well with MOS computer peripheral devices such as the 6522 VIA (versatile interface adaptor). The input signals control electronic switches which are connected into a complex resistor network. This network is called an "R2R" type, because it incorporates resistors of only two values. It does not matter what value these resistors have, provided the higher value components have precisely double the value of the lower value components. An R2R digital to analogue

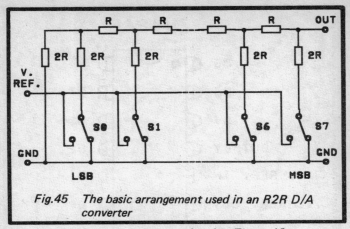

Fig.45   The basic arrangement used in an R2R D/A converter

converter uses the arrangement outlined in Figure 45.

It would take a great deal of calculating to prove it, but the output voltage is equal to the binary input value multiplied by a certain voltage. The ZN426E has a built-in 2.55 volt reference source, but it has separate reference input and output terminals so that an external reference source can be used if desired. The integral reference source is a very high quality type and there is not normally any point in using an external voltage source. Its temperature coefficient is typically 40 parts per million per degree Centigrade. The tolerance of the voltage rating is plus and minus 0.075 volts, which in percentage terms means that the actual reference voltage will be within 3% of its nominal level. An 8 bit input provides 256 different output levels, and in terms of decimal input values the range is 0 to 255. This gives an output voltage which is equal to the input value multiplied by 10 millivolts (0.01 volts).

Figure 46 shows the circuit diagram for a simple power supply based on the ZN426E. This utilizes the internal reference source, and the maximum output voltage of IC1 is therefore 2.55 volts. R1 is the load resistor for the reference circuit, and C1 is a decoupling capacitor. IC2 and TR1 act as a voltage amplifier and a buffer stage respectively. VR1 is adjusted to give a voltage gain of 20dB

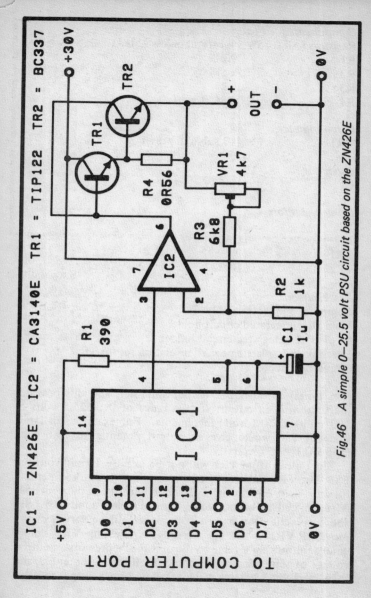

Fig.46 A simple 0–25.5 volt PSU circuit based on the ZN426E

87

Components for Figure 46
Resistors (All 0.25W 5% carbon unless noted)

R1	390R
R2	1k
R3	6k8
R4	0R56 1 watt

Potentiometer

VR1	4k7 sub-min preset

Capacitor

C1	1µ 63V elect

Semiconductors

IC1	ZN426E
IC2	CA3140E
TR1	TIP122
TR2	BC337

Miscellaneous
Computer connector and lead
8 pin DIL integrated circuit holder
14 pin DIL integrated circuit holder
Heatsink and "plastic power" insulation set for TR1
Circuit board, etc.

(ten times) through the output amplifier, and this provides the unit with an output voltage range of 0 to 25.5 volts in 100 millivolt (0.1 volt) increments. For example, an input value of 156 would give an output potential of 15.6 volts (156 × 0.1 = 15.6 volts).

The output from TR1 will not be exactly 10 millivolts per LSB, but VR1 can trim the voltage gain of IC2 to compensate for any slight error in IC1. The non-linearity of the converter is guaranteed to be no worse than plus and minus 0.5 LSB, and in practice the output voltages should be very accurate provided VR1 is set up correctly. Adjusting VR1 simply entails outputting a value to the unit that represents an output voltage of something approaching the full scale potential, and then carefully adjusting VR1 for the correct output voltage.

For example, a value of 200 could be written to the supply, and then VR1 would be adjusted for an output of exactly 20 volts. For optimum accuracy the output voltage should be monitored with a digital multimeter when setting up VR1. The supply is capable of greater accuracy than most analogue multimeters.

The accuracy at very low output voltages might not be very good due to small offset voltages in both IC1 and IC2. These could be counteracted by fitting an offset null control to IC2, but in practice this is probably not worthwhile. It is unlikely that output voltages of less than about 500 millivolts would ever be required, and it is only at these low voltages that an offset null control would significantly improve results.

R2 and TR2 form a conventional current limiting circuit, and the specified value for R4 sets the maximum output current at about 1 amp. The value of R4 can obviously be changed to suit other maximum output currents, but the circuit can not handle currents of much more than about 2 amps. The value for R4 (in ohms) is equal to 0.55 divided by the required maximum output current (in amps). For maximum output currents of more than a few tens of milliamps TR1 will require a heatsink, and for outputs of around one or two amps a substantial heatsink will be required.

It is assumed in Figure 46 that the digital to analogue converter circuit will be powered from a computer or other controller, but if necessary it can be powered from the main supply via a 5 volt monolithic voltage regulator circuit. The maximum current consumption for the ZN426E is only 9 milliamps (typically 5 milliamps), but note that this does not include the 6.3 milliamps drawn by reference voltage circuit. This still gives a worse case current consumption of only 15 milliamps, and a low power regulator should be capable of providing this.

The input voltage to the main circuit is given as 30 volts, but this is the minimum figure needed to ensure that the full 25.5 volt maximum output potential can be achieved. The maximum supply voltage is 36 volts, which is imposed by the CA3140E used in the IC2 position. In order to obtain an input supply that keeps within these limits over the full output current range it will be necessary to use a mains transformer having a generous current rating in the circuit that provides the unregulated input. One having a current rating about twice as high as would normally be used should suffice. A better alternative is to use a circuit that provides a regulated output voltage of about 30 to 33 volts. If this method is adopted the mains transformer will need to have a secondary voltage rating that is a little higher than would be needed if the regulator circuit was not included, but by giving a much more stable input supply it will improve the line regulation performance of the unit.

Driving The Unit

With so many different home computers now in circulation it is impossible to give details on how to connect the unit to even a significant fraction of them. Unless you have a reasonable understanding of computer interfacing in general, and interfacing your particular model of computer in particular, you would be well advised not to try a project of this type. Well, not until you have gained the necessary knowledge and experience anyway. Home computers are generally quite tolerant of inappropriately connected hardware, but if any damage should occur it could be extremely expensive to have it repaired. The computer must have some sort of parallel output port that has at least eight latching outputs, although this could be in the form of some sort of add-on board if the computer does not have a suitable port built in.

Ideally the unit would be driven from a user port such as those which form part of the standard complement of interfaces on the Commodore 64, Commodore VIC-20, and BBC model B (and most subsequent BBC machines such as the Master 128). Taking the BBC machine as an example, inputs D0 to D7 of the power supply circuit would be driven from lines PB0 to PB7 of the user port. One of the ground lines would be connected to the "0V" line of the supply circuit, and one of the +5 volt lines would be used to supply power to the +5 volt input of the supply circuit.

In common with many parallel ports, the BBC computer's user port can act as an eight bit input or an eight bit output, or it can even operate in a split mode with some lines as inputs and others as outputs. Obviously all eight lines must act as outputs in this application, but the user port lines all default to the input mode at switch-on. They can be set to operate as outputs by writing a value of 255 to the data direction register at address &FE62 (e.g. ?&FE62 = 255). This address is only used for setting the user port lines as inputs or outputs, and data for the supply circuit must be written to address &FE60. For instance, the command "?&FE60 = 200" would be used to set the output potential at 20 volts.

Digital control could be taken further, and the controlling circuit could be used to set the current limit level. This could be achieved by having a few digital output lines controlling relays via simple common emitter driver circuits. A set of contacts on each relay would connect a resistor into circuit when closed, and by activating the appropriate relay the desired current limiting resistor could be switched into circuit. Whether it would be worthwhile doing so is another matter. Few computers provide sufficient output lines to permit this without resorting to an add-on interface of some kind. It would seem to offer little advantage anyway, since the current limit level could be set just as easily by a switch on the supply unit as it could via the computer.

This circuit does not have to be controlled by way of a computer or some other highly sophisticated microprocessor circuit. Even something as basic as a binary up/down counter driven via a manually gated low frequency clock oscillator would suffice. This would not permit automatic testing, but it would be a viable alternative to a conventional bench power supply unit. A voltmeter could be used to give a display of the output voltage, or it should be possible to successfully drive a simple digital display circuit from the 8 bit binary control signal. A simple keypad and decoder circuit is another possible source for the control signal. There is plenty of scope here for the electronics experimenter.

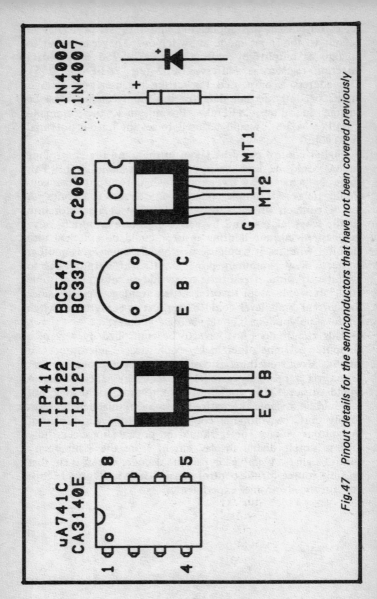

Fig.47 Pinout details for the semiconductors that have not been covered previously

92